Food Preparation and Cooking, with Food Service

To be used in conjunction with the following:

Practical Cookery (EIGHTH EDITION)

The Theory of Catering (EIGHTH EDITION)

Food and Drink Service (ROY HAYTER, MACMILLAN, 1996)

Hodder & Stoughton

A MEMBER OF THE HODDER HEADLINE GROUP

Victor Ceserani MBE, CPA, MBA, FHCIMA
Formerly Head of the Ealing School of Hotelkeeping and Catering (now Thames Valley University)

and

Professor David Foskett Bed (Hons), FHCIMA
Associate Dean, School of Tourism, Hospitality and Leisure, Thames Valley University, London

Order queries: please contact Bookpoint Ltd, 39 Milton Park, Abingdon, Oxon OX14 4TD. Telephone: (44) 01235 400414, Fax: (44) 01235 400454. Lines are open from 9.00–6.00, Monday to Saturday, with a 24 hour message answering service. Email address: orders@bookpoint.co.uk.

British Library Cataloguing in Publication Data
A catalogue record for this title is available from The British Library

ISBN 0 340 70473 X

First published 1998
Impression number 10 9 8 7 6 5 4 3 2 1
Year 2003 2002 2001 2000 1998

Typeset by Wearset, Boldon, Tyne & Wear.
Printed in Great Britain for Hodder & Stoughton Educational, a division of Hodder Headline Plc, 338 Euston Road, London NW1 3BH by Scotprint Ltd, Musselburgh, Scotland.

Contents

Introduction

This workbook is designed to assist the candidate in gaining the underpinning knowledge required for the NVQ Level 1 qualification in Preparing and Serving food.

In addition to learning the basic skills of preparing and serving food it is necessary to be aware of the health, safety and hygiene factors which must be practised at all times to comply with current legislation.

The candidate must learn to understand that the theoretical aspects of the subject are often as important as the practical skills, especially if it is the intention of the candidate to progress to the more advanced skills levels.

The purpose of this book is to guide the candidate through the various units, encouraging them to develop the knowledge and understanding which will assist them in their practical assessment.

National and Scottish Vocational Qualifications (NVQ/SVQ)

A National and Scottish Vocational Qualification is awarded following a method of assessment to candidates achieving the required level of ability. These levels are:

- Level 1: Operative
- Level 2: Craft
- Level 3: Supervisory
- Level 4: Junior management

Assessment occurs at work, and/or college in a realistic working environment and is available to all irrespective of age and entry qualification requirements. The system enables the participants to progress through the levels in a flexible manner according to individual circumstances and abilities. Previous experience and knowledge are taken into account.

Candidates are fully involved in the assessment procedure by the completion of an evidence diary recording their performance. This provides evidence of activities carried out in a working environment while being assessed.

Understanding, underpinning knowledge or related theory is assessed orally or by the used of visual or other aids and, for levels 3/4, written questions may be used.

Recording assessment details

With all aspects of dealing with training, people's records must always be stored securely and available only to those authorised to have access to them.

- Past records should be valid, accurate relevant and reliable.
- Current information about learners must also be valid, accurate relevant and reliable.
- All interpretation of records must be fair and justified.

The records should be kept together and form the portfolio of evidence and may include audio and video tapes.

It is essential at the outset that all records are retained and may include:

- completed record units;
- assessment plans;
- oral/written questions used during assessment;
- any case studies or role plays used;
- work-based projects;
- accreditation of prior learning assessment plans;
- details of accreditation of prior learning advised or assessed;
- references and letters of validation;
- records of meeting with assessors and verifiers;
- certificates;
- documented feedback given to candidates.

A candidate needs to ensure that the contents of his/her portfolio are relevant to the performance criteria and range of elements being worked towards.

Maintain a safe and secure working environment

Maintain personal health and hygiene

Read: *Practical Cookery* pages 6–10: 16–17

1 What is important about the clothing, footwear and headgear that you wear at work?

....

....

2 Why should your hair be neat and tidy, worn in line with operational requirements and covered in certain work situations?

....

....

3 **a** In which type of job may jewellery, perfume and cosmetics be worn and which jobs not?

....

b What are the risks of staff working with food using perfume or aftershave?

....

4 **a** Who should treat any cuts, grazes or wounds that you may receive during your work?

....

b Should they be kept covered and, if yes, what should they be covered with and why?

....

5 a If you become ill or develop an infection, to whom should you report?

....

b Why is it essential to report any illness or infection promptly?

....

6 Write out the hygiene practices that must be adhered to within your working environment.

....

....

....

....

....

7 Why is it important that all work is carried out in an efficient and organised manner in line with organisational procedures and legal requirements?

....

....

....

8 Why must a good standard of personal hygiene be maintained at all times?

....

....

9 From your own observations and experience, what faults in personal hygiene have you found in fellow workers?

....

....

....

Carry out procedures in the event of a fire

Read: *Practical Cookery* pages 2–4

1 If a fire breaks out, how and why should you raise the alarm immediately?

2 Suggest any possible causes of fire in your own working environment.

3 How do you call the fire brigade?

Fire appliances

4 While waiting for the fire brigade what action can be taken to curtail the fire?

....

....

5 a What fire fighting equipment do you have in your workplace?

....

....

b Where are the instructions for use?

....

....

....

c Why is it essential that fire fighting equipment is correctly used in line with manufacturer's instructions and only in accordance with the procedures of your organisation?

....

....

6 a Where are the safety and emergency signs and notices in your workplace?

....

....

b Why is it essential that these be strictly followed?

....

....

7 a If a fire breaks out and evacuation of the building is required, how can you help to make this calm and orderly?

....

....

b What are the potential dangers of evacuating a building in which a fire has broken out in a *non*-orderly and calm manner?

....

....

8 When a building is being evacuated, where should all the workers assemble and why?

....

....

9 What is the purpose of a fire blanket?

....

10 Why should a fire never be approached unless it is safe to do so?

....

....

ELEMENT
NG1.3

Maintain a safe environment for customers, staff and visitors

Read: *Practical Cookery* pages 10–15

1 It is essential that hazards and potential hazards to the safety of customers, staff and visitors are promptly identified and rectified.
To whom should serious accidents be reported?

....

2 Before cleaning any electrical equipment, what should be done to the power plug?

....

3 Name three potential hazards of electricity.

....

....

....

4 What is meant by an overloaded plug?

....

5 What is the danger of not replacing a light bulb or tube when the faulty one has been removed?

....

6 Why should your hands be dry when handling electrical equipment and plugs?

....

7 How does the Health and Safety at Work Act require employers to report potential hazards?

....

8 How should customers, staff and visitors be made aware of all hazards and potential hazards in line with operational requirements?

....

....

9 Write a list of cautionary measures that can be taken to warn customers, staff and visitors of hazards and potential hazards. Illustrate your answer with some examples.

....

....

....

....

....

....

10 Why is it important that accidents, damage and non-rectifiable hazards are promptly reported to the appropriate person?

....

....

....

b Who would be the appropriate person in your establishment?

....

11 If all work is not carried out in an organised and efficient manner in line with appropriate organisational procedures and legal requirements, what could be the possible results?

....

....

....

....

12 List all the potential hazards that you have observed within your own working environment.

....

....

....

....

....

13 What should be the procedure if a suspicious package or item is found, and why?

....

....

14 Where is the First Aid equipment and accident register located in your establishment?

....

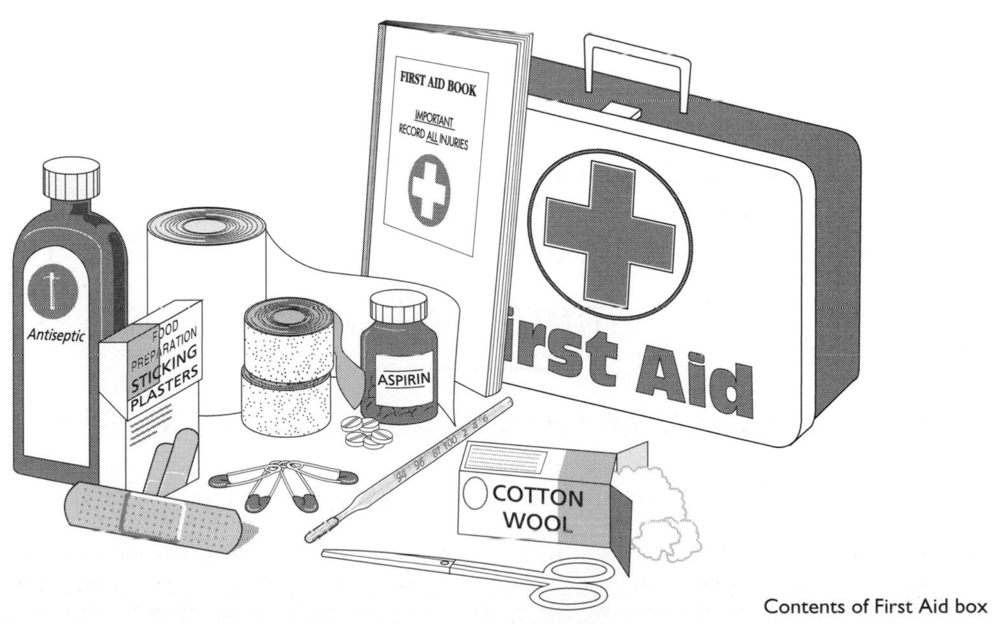

Contents of First Aid box

15 Who is responsible for First Aid in your place of work?

....

16 When lifting heavy items of equipment or packages, what may occur if the correct lifting techniques are not used?

....

....

17 Where and from whom can information on current Health and Safety legislation be obtained?

....

18 What is the employee's responsibility in relation to Health and Safety legislation?

....

....

....

....

....

....

ELEMENT
NG1.4

Maintain a secure environment for customers, staff and visitors

Read: *Practical Cookery* pages 10–15

1 Why should every employee be aware of potential security risks?

....

....

2 Within the organisation in which you work, what are the procedures for reporting identified potential security risks and to whom would you report?

....

....

3 What are the potential dangers if customer and staff areas are not properly secured against unauthorised access?

....

....

4 Unless all storage and security facilities are secured against unauthorised access, what is likely to happen?

....

....

5 What particular items in your establishment are vulnerable to theft?

....

....

6 How is any loss of property by staff or customers dealt with and to whom should it be reported?

....

....

7 Which keys, property and areas should be secured from unauthorised access at all times?

....

....

8 Why is it essential to be aware of potential security risks? Illustrate your answer with 3 examples.

....

....

....

9 If proper procedures are not followed with regard to lost property, what can possibly happen?

....

....

10 a Why is it essential to comply with Health and Safety legislation?

....

....

b What can be the results of failure to comply with Health and Safety legislation?

....

....

11 Where and from whom can information on current Health and Safety legislation be obtained?

....

12 Why should only disclosable information be given to others?

....

....

13 a Why is it important to report all unusual or non-routine incidents to the appropriate person?

....

....

b Give two suggested examples, and to whom would you report them?

....

....

....

Record of Achievement – Completion of Unit NG1	
Candidate's signature:	....
Assessor's signature:	....
Date:	....

UNIT
ING3
Maintain customer care

Deal with customers

Read: *The Theory of Catering* pages 338–347

Catering staff serving at food service counters directly to customers may be employed in canteens, refectories, dining halls and so on, in schools, hospitals, industrial establishments, offices and other establishments. Other food outlets include fast food establishments such as crêperies, baked potato houses, McDonald's, fish and chip shops and take aways, buffets at all kinds of functions including outdoor catering, wedding receptions and carveries. It is important that staff working in these areas provide customer satisfaction.

1 When dealing with customers it is important to smile and be po................ and car................ towards customers.

2 It is important to put the customer first and

a make them feel C................ ;

b make them feel G................ ;

c make them feel I................ ;

d make them want to return to your restaurant or establishment.

3 It is important when you are dealing with customers that you adjust your behaviour to suit certain customers.

True ☐ **False** ☐

4 Should we treat all customers equally?

Yes ☐ **No** ☐

5 Give customers your time and full attention. We must concentrate on our appearance. The way we react with our body sends messages to the customer. This is known as body language, therefore we must be smart at all times.

What other things must we do that will affect our appearance?

....

....

6 A telephone call must be answered within three rings.

True ☐ **False** ☐

7 Finding out what makes customers happy will affect our business. Why?

....

....

8 What do you think makes your customers happy?

....

....

9 Customers expect to be looked after. They also want to see a good after-sales service. What else do you think they want to see in a restaurant?

....

....

10 Customer care gives the caterer the opportunity to be 'special' to win customers. What does your restaurant or establishment do to make customers special?

....

11 A loyalty scheme can be as simple as giving regular customers discount – for example, a clubcard.

What establishment or organisation do you know that uses a clubcard?

....

....

12 When a customer comes into contact with you, the caterer, the image of your establishment is being exposed. Try to describe your company's image or a company image you know about. For example:

- Caring, value for money, quality
- Young image, fashionable, reasonably priced
- ....
- ....

13 When a restaurant manager remembers a customer's name, many customers are delighted, but if staff treat customers badly, they will often not return to the restaurant. Unhappy customers react by making the staff unhappy, and this will affect the business.

Happy staff **Happy customers**

leads to

....

14 The caterer must set standards for customer care and train the staff.

Performance must be measured and rewarded.

The staff must know what the company stands for. This is known as the 'mission statement'.

The staff must also know what behaviour the company values highly. Why?

....

....

15 A waiter or waitress in a restaurant must know the menu and what the dishes are comprised of.

a Is this good customer care?

Yes ☐ **No** ☐

b If yes, what other information should the waiter or waitress know about the menu?

....

....

16 Tick which of the following are good examples of customer care phases:

☐ 'I'll take care of that for you right away'
☐ 'Sorry, I'm too busy to deal with you'
☐ 'I'll go and get it for you myself'
☐ 'Forget it, you're making too much of a fuss'
☐ 'Sorry too late, we have run out of that dish, have something else'
☐ 'I'll be glad to help you'
☐ 'Is there anything else I can help you with?'
☐ 'No, sorry – too late, come back tomorrow'
☐ 'I don't know, but I'll find out now. Please take a seat for a moment'
☐ 'Sorry for the delay, you will just have to be more patient'

17 Informing the staff of what is going on is an important element in customer care.

True ☐ **False** ☐

18 Good interested staff will help promote customer care.

True ☐ **False** ☐

19 A good team spirit is important in customer care.

True ☐ **False** ☐

20 Standards are important in customer care.

- The entrance door should be clean and tidy, the doors should be marked 'welcome'.
- The customer must then be greeted by whom?...............
- The staff should be smartly dressed and well ....
- Customers are escorted to the table by whom? ....
- If there is a delay, staff apologise and an explanation is given to the customer. In the event of a delay in the service, give an example of how you would apologise to the customer.

  ....

  ....
- At the end of the meal, who escorts the customer to the door?

  ....
- What should this person say to the customer?

  ....

21 In some organisations customers are called G...............

22 If a customer is rude or aggressive to a waiter or waitress, should the waiter or waitress be rude or aggressive in return?

Yes ☐ **No** ☐

23 When dealing with customers, behaviour should be:

- understanding – learn to understand customers' needs;

- patient – learn to be patient with all customers;
- show interest and be enthusiastic. Also (complete the following)

Wel...............

help...............

pol...............

car...............

24 Customers' needs and requirements must be acted upon without delay. Why?

....

....

ELEMENT
ING3.2

Deal with customer incidents

1 When a customer makes a comment about the restaurant or the meal, who should you tell?

....

2 When dealing with customers, it is important to make sure that the restaurant is hygienic and safe.

How can you make sure the restaurant is safe for customers? Give some examples.

- By making sure that the carpets have not lifted and therefore may cause the customer to trip over.

....

....

....

3 All customer complaints must be dealt with without delay. Why?

....

4 If a customer has lost something, what should you do?

....

5 If a waiter or waitress spills wine on a customer, how should you act?

....

....

6 If a customer spills water or wine on the table, how should you act?

....

....

7 If a customer breaks a glass or drops a tray of food from a self-service counter, what should you do?

....

....

8 It is important that a customer incident is dealt with immediately and calmly so that the customer does not feel

9 Treat all customers with courtesy. Treat people with disabilities as people with ability, and forget the **dis**.

Talk to people in wheelchairs. Do not talk through them.

How would you deal with someone in a wheelchair who had been escorted to the restaurant?

....

....

10 How would you deal with a customer who has a language difficulty?

....

....

11 How would you deal with a customer who has a disability that affects the control of their hands?

....

....

Record of Achievement – Completion of Unit 1NG3	
Candidate's signature:	....
Assessor's signature:	....
Date:	....

UNIT
ING4

Develop effective working relationships

Create and maintain effective working relationships with other members of staff

Read: *Practical Cookery* pages 17–22

1 What are you doing at present? What are your responsibilities and to whom are you responsible?

....

....

2 If any of your colleagues asks you to do something that can be met within your responsibility, why should you be prepared to do it promptly and co-operatively?

....

....

3 From your experience, how are helpful relationships made? Give two examples.

a ....

b ....

4 If you require help from a colleague, why is it best to ask politely?

....

....

5 In a busy situation you may receive information which is also intended for other colleagues. Why is it important to pass it on promptly and accurately?

....

....

6 You may be given some confidential information. Why should you be cautious about passing this on? Support your answer with an example.

....

....

....

7 If you find disagreements or arguments cause conflict, how are these best

a discussed;

....

....

b resolved;

....

....

c reported accurately and promptly to the appropriate person.

....

....

d Give an example from your experience showing how points **a**, **b** and **c** were met.

....

....

....

....

8 What in your opinion are the advantages of teamwork in a working situation?

....

....

....

9 List the various ways in which teamwork can be carried out.

....

....

....

Manager briefing chefs

10 In the work situation certain items of equipment are used by various people.

a What should be the golden rule followed by each worker when they have finished using the equipment and before going off duty?

....

....

....

b Give examples of bad habits that you have observed.

....

....

....

11 How do you react to criticism of your work

a by a colleague

....

b by your supervisor

....

....

12 What type of criticism do you react best to? Give an example.

....

....

13 What are your responsibilities in complying with Equal Opportunities legislation?

....

....

14 List the various methods of relaying essential information and knowledge to other staff, particularly those with special needs.

....

....

....

....

15 What do you consider is the effect on production outputs of good working relationships?

....

....

....

16 List the factors that influence relationships.

....

....

....

Greet and assist visitors Health and Safety

Read: *Practical Cookery* pages 2–4: 10–15: 16–17

1 List the security procedures in your establishment.

....

....

....

2 Why is it important to comply with these procedures?

....

....

....

3 Name any potential hazards within your establishment.

....

....

....

4 What should you do if you find a suspicious item or package?

....

....

5 Give 3 examples of major injury examples.

....

....

....

6 Where is the First Aid and accident register located in your establishment?

....

7 All accidents must be reported to the employer and a record of the accident entered in the ....

8 When an accident occurs the member of staff responsible for First Aid must be called immediately. Name 3 common types of accidents.

....

....

....

9 In the case of a severe accident an ambulance must be called.

What number should be dialled to call an ambulance?

....

Full name of injured person:			
Occupation:		Supervisor:	
Time of accident:	Date of accident:	Time of report:	Date of report:
Nature of injury or condition:			
Details of hospitalisation:			
Extent of injury (after medical attention)			
Place of accident or dangerous occurance			
Injured person's evidence of what happened (include equipment/items/or other persons): Use separate sheet if necessary			
Witness evidence (1):		Witness evidence (2):	
Supervisor's recommendations:			
Date:	Supervisor's signature This form must be sent to the company health and safety officer		

Accident report form

10 Where should you keep any money or valuables while you are at work?

....

11 If you are to be able to assist visitors, you should understand the structure of the organisation in which you work.

Draw a sketch plan in the box over the page and name the various parts of your organisation (see also Question 12).

....

....

....

....

12 Show the responsibilities of relevant people in your organisation and their location on your sketch plan.

Customer care

Read: *The Theory of Catering* pages 338–347

13 What are the main requirements of persons with special mobility needs?

....

....

....

14 How can assistance be given to persons having special mobility needs?

....

....

....

15 In what way are customers and visitors greeted in your organisation:

a when they arrive? ....

b when they depart? ....

16 What are your responsibilities in complying with the organisation's policies and procedures with regard to customers and visitors?

....

....

....

17 What are your responsibilities in complying with Equal Opportunities legislation?

....

....

Communication

18 a What are the main forms of verbal and non-verbal communication?

....

....

b How do you recognise and react to them?

19 a Why is it important to recognise and react to verbal and non-verbal communication?

b What can happen in an organisation if communication by either verbal or non-verbal means breaks down?

20 What in your opinion arc thc most common special communication needs people might have?

21 How do you communicate with persons having special communication needs?

22 What do you understand by 'effective spoken communication'?

23 Why is effective spoken communication essential when greeting and assisting visitors and customers?

24 What rules apply to confidentiality of information?

....

....

....

Record of Achievement – Completion of Unit ING4	
Candidate's signature:	....
Assessor's signature:	....
Date:	....

UNIT
1ND2

Handle and maintain knives

Read: *Practical Cookery* pages 26–32

1 Why is it important to keep knives clean and to satisfy food hygiene regulations?

....

2 Why is it important to keep knife blades sharp?

To comply with food safety?

....

To carry out knife work efficiently?

....

3 What are the dangers of working with blunt knives?

....

....

4 List the safety rules for knife handling.

....

....

....

5 How can cross-contamination be prevented when using knives for different foods?

....

Set out a suggested colour coding for knife handles to be used for different foods.

....

....

6 Why is it important to select the correct knife for specific jobs from the safety point of view?

....

for working efficiently? Give examples.

....

....

7 Why should meat never be boned out or fish filleted from the frozen state?

....

8 What is the correct way to sharpen knife blades? What is the procedure for keeping them sharp at all times?

....

....

9 What are the essential requirements for stainless steel knives? What advantages have they got over other knives?

....

....

Basic set of knives

Record of Achievement – Completion of Unit IND2	
Candidate's signature:	....
Assessor's signature:	....
Date:	....

UNIT

IND12

Maintain hygiene in food storage, preparation and cooking

Maintain hygiene in food storage

Read: *Practical Cookery* pages 43–56; *The Theory of Catering* pages 529–536.

1 What are the essential requirements for washing of hands which must be done in every area where food is handled?

....

....

2 What is the correct method of washing and drying of the hands?

....

....

3 If hands are not washed thoroughly and frequently before commencing work and during the handling of food, what are the dangers?

....

....

Germs or bacteria can be transferred on to anything with which the body comes into contact. Personal cleanliness is essential to prevent germs getting into food.

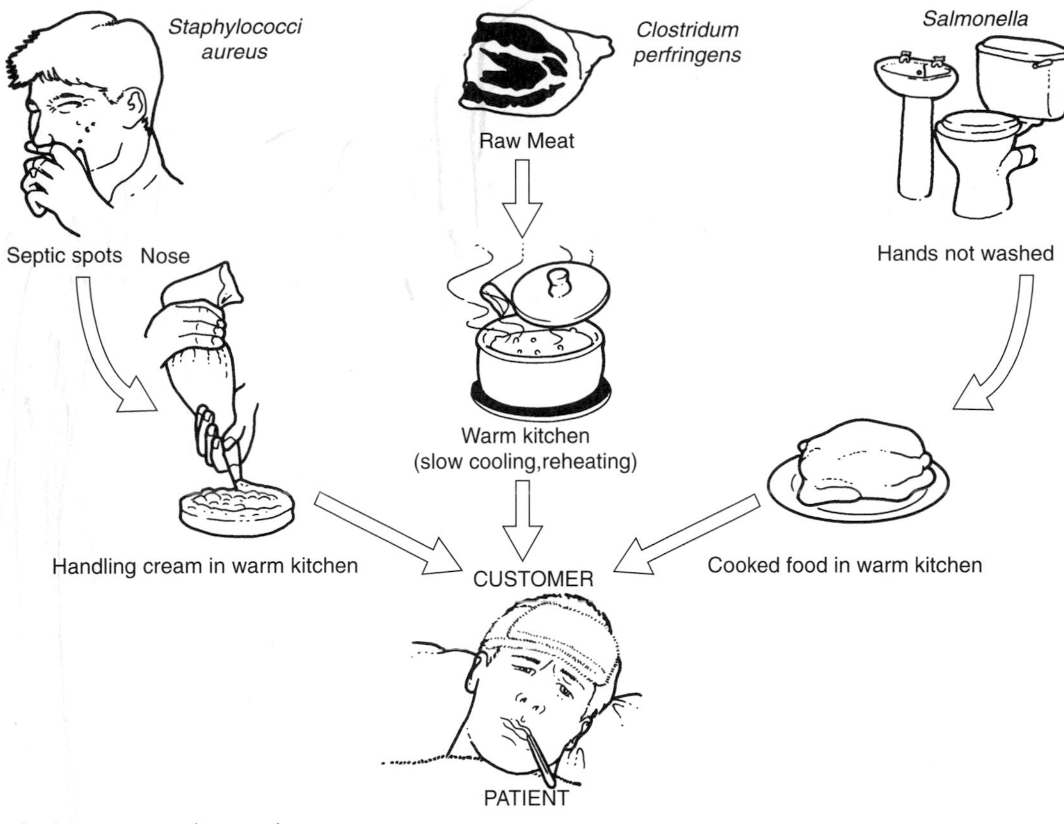

How food poisoning may be caused

4 Why should hands be thoroughly washed after

a handling food waste;

....

b visiting the toilet;

....

c handling unwashed fresh foods;

....

d smoking;

....

e handling cleaning fluids, materials

....

5 Read *The Theory of Catering* pages 305–6.

This sets out the requirements for the cleanliness and safety of storage areas. After reading this write about any examples of bad practice that you have observed together with the reasons why you think this happened.

....

....

....

6 Why is it essential that deliveries of food items are reported promptly to the appropriate person?

....

....

7 If the policy in Question 6 is not carried out what are the dangers with regard to:

a meat/poultry/fish;

....

b dairy products;

....

c vegetables or fruit;

....

d eggs;

....

e dry goods

....

8 Where and how should all the above items be stored?

....

....

....

....

9 Storing foods at the correct temperature is important if it is to be kept in good condition. What are the correct hygiene storage conditions, giving temperatures where appropriate, for the following groups of foods?

a Ambient ....

b Chilled ....

c Frozen ....

d Cooked ....

e Uncooked ....

10 Unexpected situations can occur in any organisation, for example early or late deliveries; non-deliveries; incorrect deliveries; problems with equipment and so on.

Why is it important that any such situations are dealt with effectively and the appropriate people informed where necessary? Support your answer with 3 examples.

....

....

....

....

....

....

11 Why is it essential that current relevant legislation relating to safe and hygienic working practices when storing food is observed at all times, and what are the penalties if this is not carried out? (Refer to the Food Safety Act.)

....

....

12 Read *The Theory of Catering* pages 364–365

What can be the result if safe working practices are not followed when storing food?

....

....

13 Read *The Theory of Catering* pages 555–559.

What should you do if you see any signs of pest infestation in food delivery and storage areas?

....

....

14 Read *The Theory of Catering* pages 542–571.

Why is good personal hygiene essential when handling and storing food?

15 Referring to the previous question, give 3 examples of bad practice that you have observed.

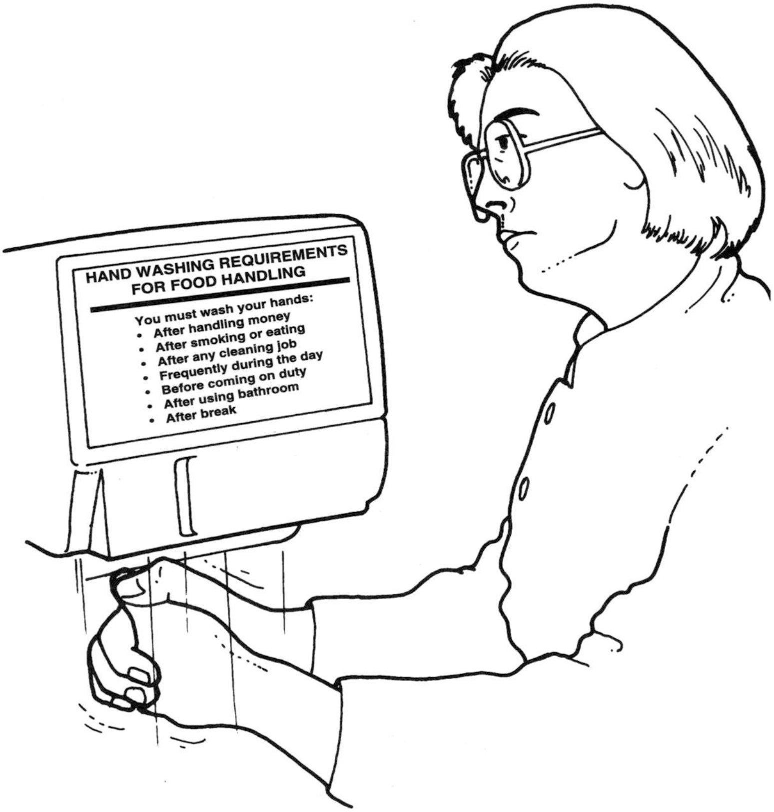

16 What can be the result if storage areas and equipment are not properly cleaned and kept in a hygienic condition? Give 3 examples of bad practice that you have seen.

17 a What is meant by the term 'high risk foods'?

....

....

b Give 4 examples of high risk foods.

....

....

....

....

c Why is it essential that high risk foods be stored and handled correctly?

....

....

18 What are the dangers if prepared food is not stored at a safe temperature before use? Mention 3 foods in your answer.

....

....

....

19 What is the significance of time and temperature when storing food?

....

....

....

Maintain hygiene in food storage

1 Read: *Practical Cookery* page 44.
Write about any bad practices that you have observed which contravene the

chart on page 44 of the above book.

....

....

....

2 Read *Practical Cookery* pages 16–17.

a What does a 'professional appearance' mean to you?

....

....

b What can it mean to other people, particularly customers?

....

....

3 Why should you not touch your nose and mouth when handling food?

....

....

4 If you have a slight cold is it better to use tissues or a handkerchief, and why?

....

5 What is the correct way to taste foods during preparation?

....

....

6 What type of dressing should be put on a cut, graze or burn, and why?

....

....

7 Why is it important to keep preparation and cooking areas and equipment hygienic when preparing and cooking food? Refer to deep frying, fish, meat and pastry work in your answer.

....

....

....

....

8 What do you understand by 'cross-contamination'? Support your answer with examples.

....

....

....

....

9 Describe 3 contamination threats that you have seen when food has been prepared and cooked.

....

....

....

....

10 What is the importance of time and temperature when preparing and cooking food? Give examples of any bad practice that you may have seen.

....

....

11 What is likely to happen if waste bins are not kept covered at all times?

....

....

12 List 4 'high risk foods' and state why they should be prepared and cooked correctly.

....

....

....

....

13 What are the correct procedures for defrosting foods such as

a large joints of meat;

....

....

b small cuts of chicken;

....

....

c whole chickens;

....

....

d fish fillets

....

....

Frozen chickens defrosting in a refrigerator

Record of Achievement – Completion of Unit IND12	
Candidate's signature:	....
Assessor's signature:	....
Date:	....

UNIT INC1

Prepare and clear areas for table and tray service

Prepare service areas and equipment for table and tray service

Read: *Food and Drink Service*, Roy Hayter, Macmillan, 1996, pages 45–47

In order for the service period to go smoothly, preparation is all-important. It is essential to make sure all the *mise-en-place* is done before the customers arrive.

1 What is the purpose of a restaurant rota?

2 Why is it important to keep preparation areas tidy?

3 Write an example of a cleaning schedule using the chart on page 42.

Sun	Mon	Tues	Wed

4 Compile a standard for restaurant tables.

....

....

....

....

....

....

5 State what you should do if you come across damaged items.

....

....

6 What is the purpose of a requisition form?

....

....

DEPARTMENTAL REQUISTION BOOK 267

Date ____________ Class ____________

Description	Quan	Unit	Price per Unit	Issued if Different	Quan	Unit	Price per Unit	Code	£	

7 Complete the following cleaning schedule for food trolleys, or copy down one which you work from daily.

a Wash tops and shelves

b ....

c ....

d ....

e ....

f ....

8 Caring for china in a restaurant is very important. Write down how china should be looked after in a catering establishment.

....

....

....

....

....

....

9 How should cutlery and silverware be cared for?

....

....

....

....

10 How should glassware be cared for?

....

....

....

....

....

11 How can a waiter or waitress help to reduce glass stress?

....

....

....

12 Why should glasses not be exposed to sudden changes in temperature?

....

....

13 If you are going to fill a glass with a hot drink, what should you do first?

....

14 Give examples of condiments and accompaniments which form part of the *mise-en-place* in the restaurant.

a Seasonings

....

....

b Sugars and sweeteners

....

....

c Prepared sauces and dressings

....

....

d Breads or rolls

....

....

15 How should the following be stored when not in use?

a Bottled sauces

....

....

b Marmalades and jams

....

....

16 What should you do if stock has passed its shelf-life?

....

17 How should broken glass be dealt with in a restaurant?

....

18 How should the following be dealt with?

a Liquid waste

....

b Empty ashtrays

....

Prepare customer dining areas for table or tray service

Read: *Food and Drink Service*, Roy Hayter, Macmillan, 1996
pages 47–49; 114–117

1 Complete the following sequence in laying up a table.

a Lay the cloth. The table top should be fully covered and between

.... cm and .... of cloth ....

b Lay and position place mats or ....

....

c ....

....

....

d Place the side...

....

e Place the napkins..

....

f Position..

....

2 When should the butter or any other items be placed on the table?

....

....

3 State what is wrong with the *à la carte* setting on page 47.

....

....

4 Give four examples of napkin folds using diagrams or sketches.

5 Give 3 examples of how menus can be used to promote the restaurant.

....

....

....

6 Give examples of 4 different types of functions, for example a wedding.

a ....

b ....

c ....

d ....

7 What is the purpose of a table plan?

....

8 What is the purpose of a function sheet?

....

9 Write down an example of a wine bar food servery set up.

....

....

....

....

....

....

10 Outline the ways in which you may have to adjust the restaurant environment in order to make customers more comfortable.

....

....

....

....

Clear dining and service areas after service

1 State how the dining room where you work has to be cleared after service. Write down a task list to demonstrate this.

....

....

....

....

....

....

2 How should soiled linen be dealt with?

....

....

3 How should dirty cutlery and crockery be dealt with when it is returned to the wash-up?

....

....

....

4 How should clean crockery and cutlery be dealt with when it comes out of the dishwasher or handwashing?

....

....

....

....

....

....

5 When carrying heavy trays, what particular safety points should you consider?

....

....

....

....

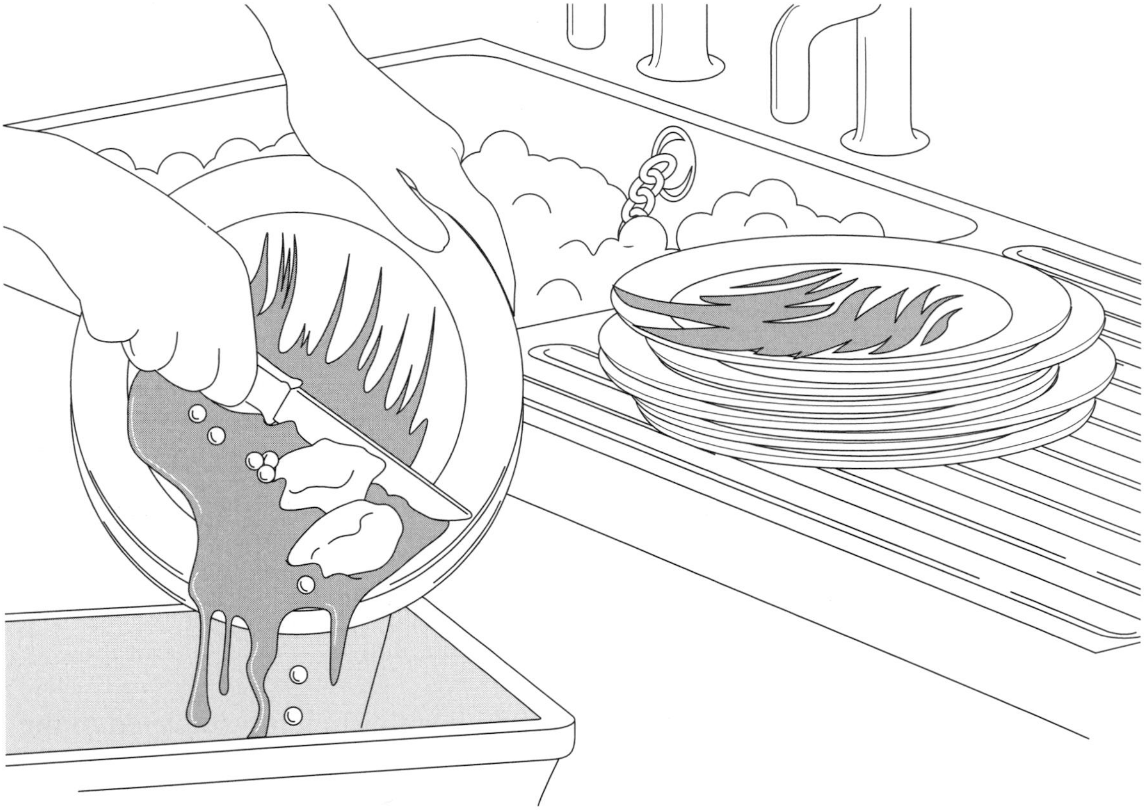

Scrape plates thoroughly before washing

6 How should the following be dealt with after the service period?

a Hot cupboards

....

b Plate warmers

....

c Refrigerated Units

....

d Trolleys

....

7 Give examples of some of the legislation which covers the activities in the restaurant.

....

....

....

....

....

....

8 Give an example of an unexpected situation you had to deal with in a restaurant where you work or have worked.

....

....

....

....

9 Draw a lay-up of a breakfast tray service suitable for an establishment of your choice.

Type of establishment:..

10 Draw an example of a banquet lay-up for one cover.

11 What health and safety legislation should the waiter or waitress be aware of when working in the restaurant?

....

....

....

....

12 What security checks should be carried out at the end of service?

....

....

Record of Achievement – Completion of Unit INC1	
Candidate's signature:	....
Assessor's signature:	....
Date:	....

UNIT

INC2

Provide a table or tray service

Greet customers and take orders

Read: *Food and Drink Service*, Roy Hayter, Macmillan, 1996, pages 51–55

Greeting and taking customers' orders is often the first line of contact the customer has with the restaurant and its staff, and therefore begins to create the overall impression.

1 Name the different ways in which orders can be taken in a catering establishment, for example written orders.

....

....

....

2 In which establishments would you expect a form to be used for the customer to place an order?

....

....

3 Breakfast forms used in hotels are placed outside guest rooms before a certain time. Suggest a time and state why.

....

....

4 Design a simple form for a hospital breakfast menu.

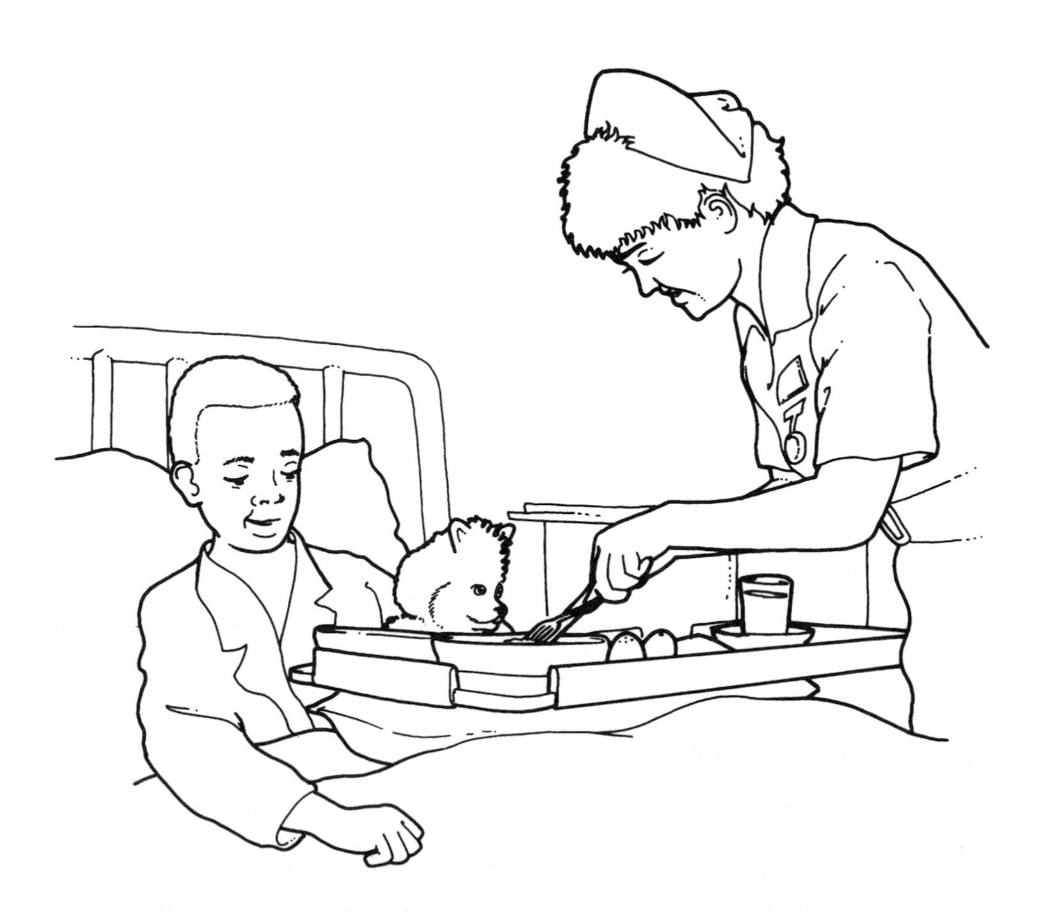

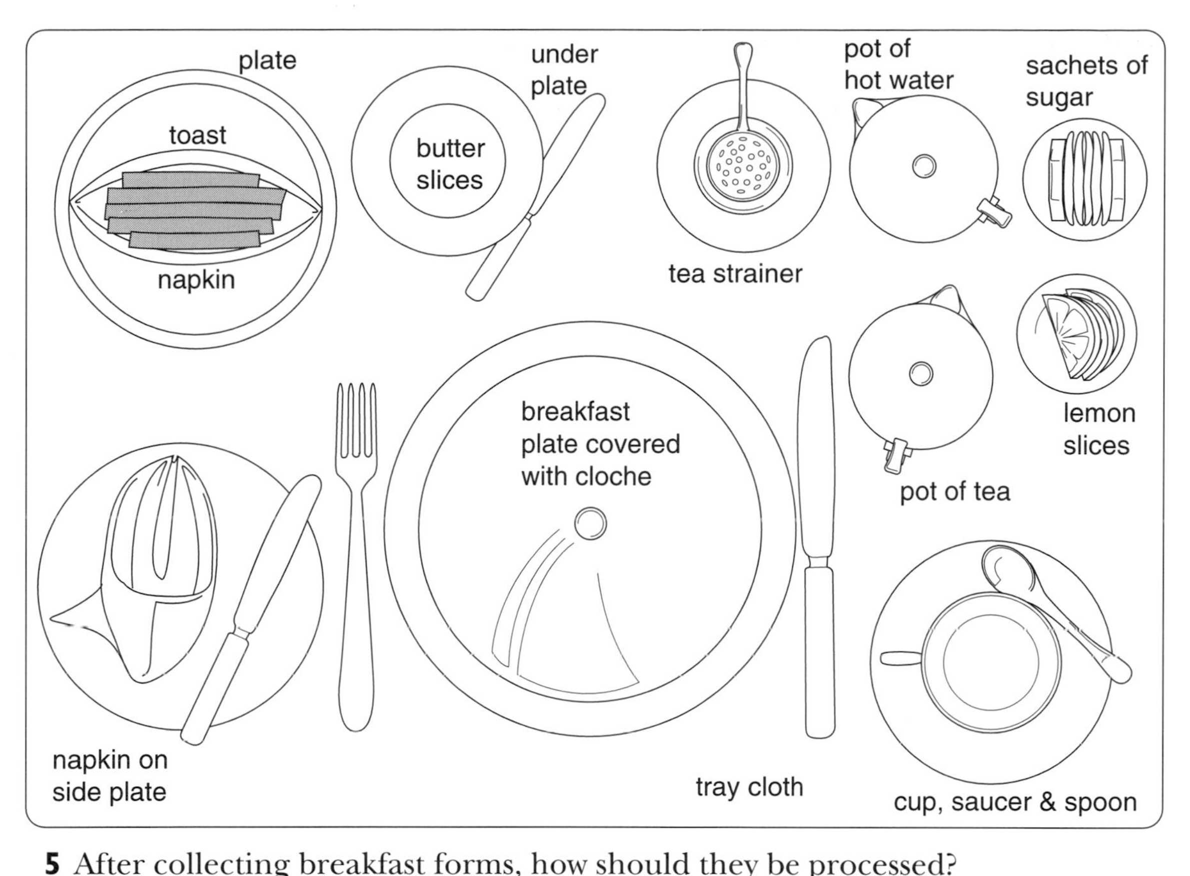

5 After collecting breakfast forms, how should they be processed?

....

....

6 When taking a telephone order, how should the telephonist greet the caller?

....

....

....

7 It is important to repeat the guest's name and room number. What else should you double check?

....

....

....

8 It is important to thank the guest and give an estimate of when the order will be delivered or confirm that it will be delivered at the ....

....

9 Before entering a guest's room with an order, what should you do?

....

10 When delivering an order to a customer, the waiter or waitress should confirm what?

....

11 It is important for a waiter or waitress to have 'product knowledge'. What is meant by the term product knowledge?

....

....

12 Describe how you have been trained to take an order in your establishment.

....

....

....

....

....

....

....

....

13 If a customer asks for a dish which is not featured on the menu, what should you do?

....

....

14 If there are a small number of dishes which the chef has created as specials, but are not featured on the main menu, how should these be communicated to the customer?

....

....

....

....

15 When communicating and describing menus to the customer, what legal requirements should the waiter or waitress be aware of?

....

....

....

16 If a customer has a difficulty when communicating with you, how should you deal with this situation?

....

....

....

17 Describe the best way of taking orders in a restaurant from a large party.

....

....

....

....

....

18 Describe how you have been trained to promote certain menu items.

....

....

....

....

....

....

19 If the menu is written in another language and it appears that some customers are experiencing real difficulties, how should you deal with this situation?

....

....

....

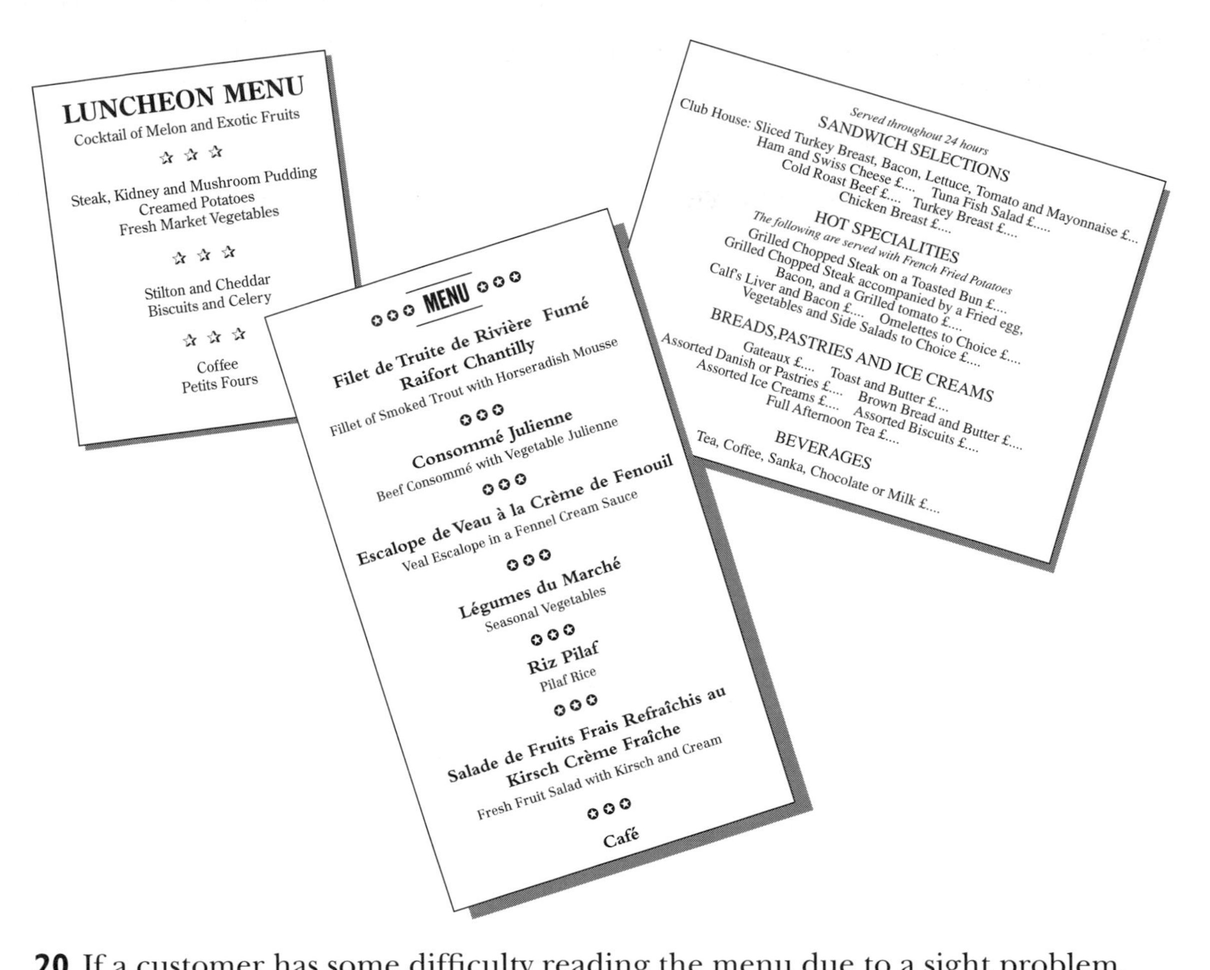

20 If a customer has some difficulty reading the menu due to a sight problem, what should you do?

....

....

21 Why should you never guess the contents of a dish for a customer?

....

....

22 Why must all information given to the customer be accurate?

....

....

23 Never leave customers waiting without an explanation or an apology. Why?

....

....

24 If customers are not greeted when they come into the restaurant, some customers will make their own way to the table. This may cause difficulties. Why?

....

....

....

25 After customers have been greeted, what should you ask them?

....

....

26 How should you greet the following customers or guests?

a VIPs

....

b Large parties

....

c People you know by name

....

27 How should customers be greeted

a when they do not have a reservation?

....

b What information do you require from these customers?

....

....

28 How should you greet a single lady customer?

....

29 If customers have to wait for a table, how should you deal with them?

....

....

....

30 How should you handle a large party in the restaurant who insist that they want the tables moved together?

....

....

31 Customers entering a restaurant seeing a number of empty tables can be suspicious. How should this be handled?

....

....

32 How should you deal with customers who have heavy coats and bags?

....

....

33 How have you been trained to escort customers to the table?

....

....

34 If customers are already seated at the table and are studying the menu by the time you arrive, how should you greet them?

....

....

35 The way in which you present menus to customers is very important. Why?

....

....

36 In what kind of establishment would you find a waiter or waitress taking an order with a terminal linked to a computer?

....

37 Copies of orders are often useful information to

a compare the amount of food purchased with the number of meals served;

b to monitor the popularity of different items;

c and ....

38 If a number of people are together at the table, whose order should you take first?

....

39 How should you deal with customers who change their mind?

....

40 If a table is set for more customers than required, how should you adjust the place settings?

....

....

....

....

....

....

41 Once the order has been taken and passed to the kitchen, it may be necessary to bring extra cutlery and remove any that is not wanted.

Write down the procedure for adjusting the cutlery.

....

....

....

....

....

....

....

....

Serve customers' orders

Read: *Food and Drink Service*, Roy Hayter, Macmillan, 1996, pages 56–59

Customers are impressed by the quality and speed of service.

1 Write down the procedure you have been taught for serving at a banquet.

....

....

....

....

....

....

2 Your workplace or training restaurant rules have to be carried out. Write down how you have been trained to serve customers in the restaurant.

....

....

....

....

....

....

3 Before taking the food to the table, what should you check?

....

4 How should ashtrays be dealt with in a restaurant?

....

....

5 a What condiments does your restaurant or establishment deal with on a daily basis?

....

....

b How are these condiments offered to the customer?

....

....

6 What is an accompaniment?

....

7 Name 4 dishes from your menu which require an accompaniment to be served.

....

....

....

....

....

....

8 Menus are structured around the accepted order of dishes. Write down what you understand as the order of dishes.

....

....

....

....

9 Personal hygiene is very important when serving food. Why?

....

....

....

....

10 How do the ways in which you present food to the customer contribute to their meal experience?

Write down what you have been taught about presenting food to the customer.

....

....

....

....

....

....

11 Give an example of adding a 'touch of theatre' to the presentation.

....

....

12 Write down the general rules for serving the food in your establishment.

For example: Serve drinks before the food.

Collect the plates before the food.

....

....

....

....

....

....

13 Give an example of how cheese is served in your restaurant.

....

....

14 If you notice during the service that a piece of equipment is damaged, what should you do?

....

....

15 When serving food, what safety precaution should you be aware of?

....

....

16 Sketch a glass to match the following drinks. Use the boxes on this page and on page 66.

Claret	**Water**	**Brandy**

Hock	**Sherry**	**Champagne**

17 Why is it important to use the most appropriate equipment when serving food and drink items?

....

....

18 Draw a diagram of a well-presented plated meal of your choice.

Dessert trolley

19 Name a selection of dishes which may be served from a trolley in the restaurant.

20 List a selection of sweeteners which may be served in a restaurant.

21 Should equipment fail or break down during the service period, what should you do?

22 If a customer spills food or wine on the table, what should you do?

Maintain dining and service areas

Read: *Food and Drink Service*, Roy Hayter, Macmillan, 1996, pages 59–60

The restaurant and dining areas should be kept tidy at all times to create a good impression with the customers, and to maintain a safe and hygienic working environment.

1 Tables should be cleared as quickly as possible. How should you deal with the following:

a Cutlery

....

b Plates

....

c Plates pushed aside by customers

....

2 Describe how plates are to be stacked in your restaurant.

....

....

3 What is the purpose of crumbing down? In what type of restaurant would you see this carried out?

....

....

....

....

4 Describe the process of clearing a table once a customer has left.

....

....

....

....

5 How should rubbish and debris be dealt with during and after the service period?

....

....

6 a Describe how soiled linen is dealt with in your establishment.

....

....

b Do you believe this to be right?

....

7 In the interests of hygiene, how should the following be dealt with after the customers have left the table?

a Clean cutlery

....

b Unused napkins

....

c Condiments

....

d Accompaniments

....

8 For reasons of safety, how should the following be dealt with?

a Spillages

....

b Breakages

....

9 After the service period has finished, how should the following be dealt with?

a Menus

....

b Sugars or sweeteners

....

c Prepared sauces and dressing

....

d Prepared bread items

10 List any promotional items that you are aware of for use in either your own restaurant or a restaurant with which you are familiar.

....

....

....

11 If a customer asks for a copy of the menu to take away, what should you do?

....

12 a Why is it important for the restaurant manager to check all stock items in use in the restaurant?

....

b Why is it necessary to maintain a constant stock of table and service items in the restaurant?

....

13 All service and dining room equipment should be checked regularly. Why?

....

14 At the end of each service period, how should the following be left:

a Tables and chairs

....

b Flowers or table decorations

....

c Floors

....

15 What is meant by a cleaning rota?

....

16 How should the floor be cleaned in your restaurant after service?

....

....

17 List any decorative items used in your restaurant and state how these are maintained.

....

....

....

....

18 What do you understand by a contract linen service?

....

....

19 If linen arrives badly laundered, what should you do?

....

20 When maintaining dining areas, list the safety and hygienic working practices that a member of staff employed in the dining room has to be aware of.

....

....

....

....

Record of Achievement – Completion of Unit INC2	
Candidate's signature:	....
Assessor's signature:	....
Date:	....

UNIT NG2

Maintain and deal with payments

Maintain the payment point

Read: *Food and Drink Service*, Roy Hayter, Macmillan, 1996, pages 37–38

Where and when customers pay for their food and beverages varies according to the type of establishment. A typical control point is the cash till.

1 In self-service restaurants, customers go to the till with their food and payment.

In table service, how and when should the bill be presented?

....

....

2 Cash tills make a record of every transaction. By operating a special key, your manager can get a total for all the transactions made during the sales period. Why is this important information?

....

....

3 Security procedures are extremely important when handling and dealing with payments. Why?

....

4 State 3 ways in which you can discourage dishonesty. For example:

- being alert to the unusual customer, who you may suspect is attempting to use a stolen card.

....

....

....

....

5 Where should the contents of the tills be placed at the end of each trading session?

....

....

6 How often should tills be checked?

....

7 Who is responsible for the cash in your establishment?

....

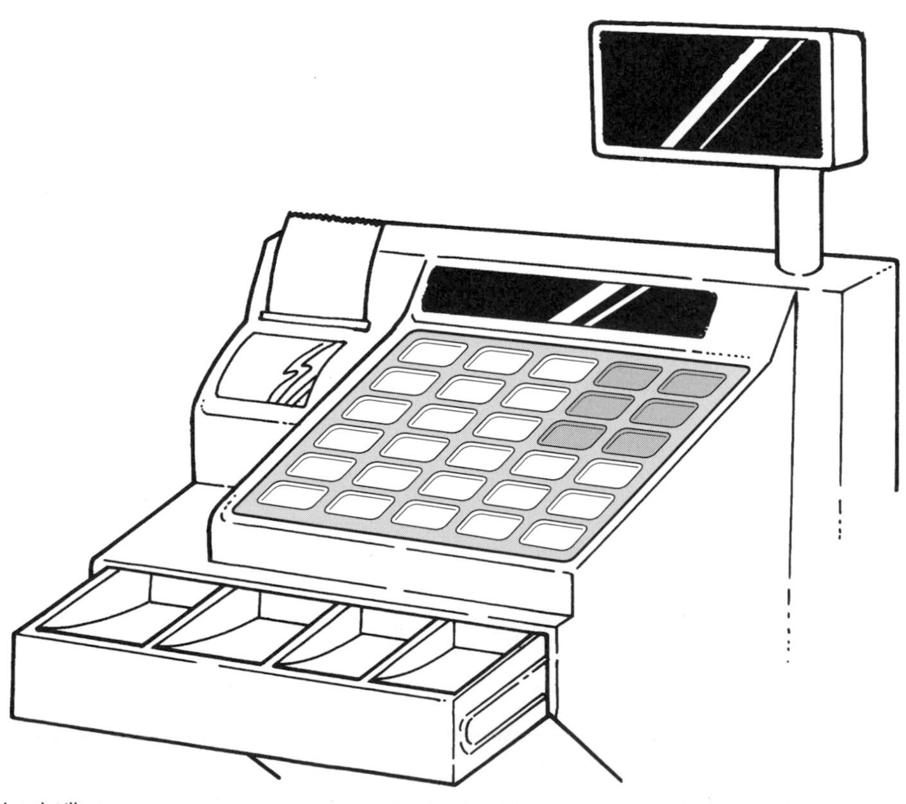

Computerised cash till

8 Workplace rules for handling cash are there to protect everyone. Give some examples of rules you are familiar with. For example:

- for customer payment by cheque guarantee card over the limit: authorisation by another member of staff must be sought with evidence of customer identification.

....

....

....

....

9 State what you understand by a security alert.

....

10 What should you do if a customer insists that you ignore the workplace rules?

....

....

11 What procedures need to be put in place for handling tips?

....

....

12 What do you understand by the term 'opening float'?

....

....

13 State the pre-opening procedure you have to carry out in your establishment before the start of trading.

....

....

....

14 Too much cash in the till is a security risk. Why?

....

....

15 During a busy trading session managers should collect cash, notes, cheques and so on from the till, and they should be placed in a bag with the till number. When should this money be counted?

....

16 Coins and notes must be kept in the proper till compartments.

True ☐ **False** ☐

17 How can differences with the actual cash and till reading occur?

....

....

....

Deal with payments

Read: *Food and Drink Service*, Roy Hayter, Macmillan, 1996, pages 38–44

1 How should prices be displayed?

....

2 Bills presented to the customer at the table should be itemised. If a customer has a query with an item, how should you deal with it?

....

....

3 How should queries be dealt with at a take-away or self-service restaurant?

....

....

....

4 To avoid confusion when handing over money, it must be made clear to the customer the value of the note, for example 'thank you, a £20 note'. What should you then do with this note?

....

5 How should you hand over the customer's change?

....

....

6 When should you report any errors or problems with customers and payment?

....

....

....

7 When dealing with customers' queries, it is important to remain polite and helpful even though some customers can get difficult when dealing with money. How can you reduce the risk of customers taking offence? For example:

- count the change into the customer's hand, onto the counter or table, or present it on a plate, whichever is the procedure in your establishment.

....

....

....

....

....

8 The bill should always be presented to the host. If you do not know who the host is, how should you present the bill?

....

....

9 How should you deal with customers with sight problems when paying their bill?

....

....

10 State the main security risks when dealing with cash.

....

....

11 If you suspect a forged note has been handed over, how should you deal with the incident?

....

....

....

12 State the difference in the following cards:

a Charge card

....

....

b Credit card

....

....

c Debit card

....

....

13 Give 1 example of the following:

a Charge card

....

b Credit card

....

c Debit card

....

14 What is meant by an Affinity Card?

....

15 What is meant by a loyalty card?

....

16 State the procedure when dealing with a credit card transaction.

....

....

....

....

....

....

17 What is a traveller's cheque and how would you deal with it?

....

....

....

....

....

18 How should you deal with a cheque payment?

....

....

....

....

19 What does EPOS stand for?

Electronic

P...............

O...............

S...............

OR

Auto...............

20 Write down the general procedure for a cash payment.

a Enter the price

....

....

b For more of the same item

....

....

c When all items are

....

....

d Enter the value

....

....

e Count the

....

....

f Count the change to

....

....

21 How should you deal with the following:

a Invalid cheques

....

....

b Authorisation refused

....

....

c Customers attempt to leave without paying

....

....

22 What aspects of safety have to be considered when dealing with payments?

....

....

....

Record of Achievement – Completion of Unit NG2	
Candidate's signature:	....
Assessor's signature:	....
Date:	....

UNIT INC3

Prepare and clear areas for counter or take-away service

Prepare areas for counter or take-away service

Read: *Food and Drink Service*, Roy Hayter, Macmillan, 1996, pages 93–94

The environment in which people consume their food and drink is very important. The surroundings should be pleasant and comfortable. A good food area must be well kept, clean, tidy and organised. Attention must be paid to detail. Hygiene is of prime importance.

1 Preparing the work areas is most important. Why?

....

....

2 When customers are waiting in a queue, it is important to make sure that promotional displays are attractive and ac................?

3 Menus and price lists should be correct at all times. For what reasons?

....

....

4 It is important to keep the service area clean, especially if this is in full view of the customer. How should the floor and walls be cleaned, and how often should they be cleaned?

....

....

5 Which areas of the restaurant must be well signposted?

....

....

6 How should broken equipment in the service area be dealt with?

....

....

7 Fire escapes must be clearly signposted and be ....

8 How should unsafe areas be dealt with?

....

....

9 How should the following be cared for in a service area?

a Brochure racks

....

....

b Newspapers

....

....

c Notice boards

....

....

10 List the procedure which should be carried out during the following times:

a Service preparation

....

....

b Pre-service check

....

....

11 Describe the following and how it should be cared for.

a Sneeze screens

....

....

b Display units

....

....

12 How should the following items of equipment be checked and cared for?

a Cutlery containers

....

....

b Lowerators

....

....

13 Describe how the following items should be presented for service.

a Glasses

....

....

b Plates

....

....

c Cups and saucers

....

....

d Napkin dispensers

....

....

14 The details of the menu should indicate what small serving equipment is required for the operation. Each dish should have its own serving equipment. Why?

....

....

15 Suggest a piece of serving equipment for the following dishes.

Dish	**Serving Equipment**
Soup	
Poached fish in a white wine sauce	
Vegetarian Lasagne	
Goulash with noodles	

Dish	Serving Equipment
Steamed broccoli	
Croquette potatoes	
Apple pie with custard	
Banana fritters	

16 Describe how tables in your restaurant should be laid-up before service.

....

....

....

....

17 Why is waste a potential Safety and Hygiene risk?

....

....

18 What should you do to prevent waste from accumulating in food rooms and service areas?

....

....

19 What do you understand as promotional material?

....

....

20 What is the purpose of promotional material?

....

....

21 How can the storing and displaying of food encourage sales?

....

....

22 Ideally how long should hot food stay on the counter? What must be avoided?

....

....

23 How should the food be displayed on the counter?

....

....

24 What do you understand by a hygiene hazard?

....

....

25 How should cold and hot cabinets be treated during service?

....

....

26 Packaged food must be regularly checked. Why?

....

....

27 The intake and outlet air vents of refrigerated display cabinet must not be blocked. Why?

....

....

28 All hot food prior to service must be checked with a temperature probe. Why?

....

....

29 Name the different ways condiments and accompaniments are made available to customers.

....

....

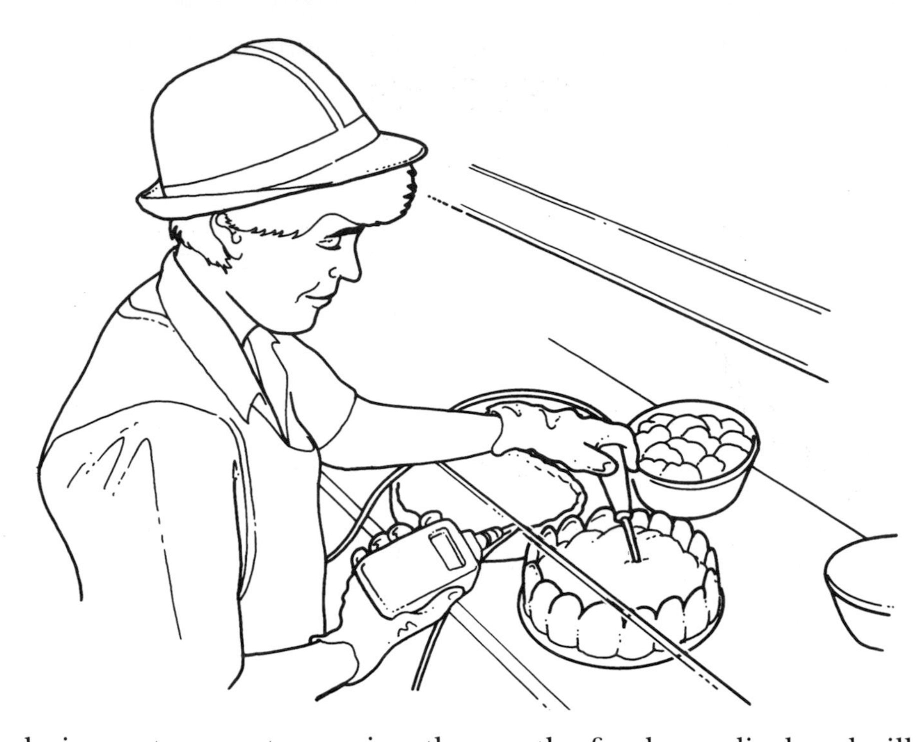

30 When laying out a counter service, the way the foods are displayed will affect the impact it has on the customer. Suggest ways in which you are able to maximise customer impact.

....

....

....

....

31 When laying-up the counter for service what must you remember *not* to do?

....

....

....

....

32 Suggest ways in which you are able to obtain a consistent standard to counter display.

....

....

....

....

Clear areas for counter or take-away

Read: *Food and Drink Service,* Roy Hayter, Macmillan, 1996, pages 93–94

1 Priority must be given to safety and a tidy environment. How should the following be left at the end of service?

a Tables and chairs

....

b Equipment

....

2 How often should cleaning solutions be changed?

....

....

3 List the Health and Safety precautions which have to be observed when cleaning heated units.

....

....

4 How should stubborn stains be dealt with?

....

....

5 How should the following be dealt with after service?

a Food containers

....

....

b Serving utensils

....

....

c Trays and cutlery

....

....

6 State how any waste should be dealt with after service.

....

....

7 What should you do with any left-over food?

....

....

8 Why is it necessary to check date marks on service food items?

....

....

9 How should the following be dealt with after service?

a Condiments and accompaniments

....

....

b Re-usable service items

....

....

10 State how the service area should be cleaned after service.

....

....

....

11 If any of the equipment breaks down during the clearing and cleaning session who should you report it to?

....

....

12 If you are clearing during the service period state what you should do if any of the following was to happen?

a A customer drops a tray of food

....

....

b Customers are not acknowledging the self-clear notice

....

....

c A customer faints in the restaurant

....

....

d A customer complains that there are no clean tables

....

....

13 What Health and Safety procedures should you be aware of when clearing the counter or service area?

....

....

14 Why should electrical equipment be turned off after service?

....

....

15 Why should waste be dispensed of carefully?

....

....

16 What are the dangers associated with waste?

....

....

....

....

17 Why is it important for food areas to be cleared after service?

....

....

18 Correct storage of food and drink which has not been sold is of vital importance. Why?

....

....

19 Do you consider the procedures for clearing service areas in your establishment to be correct? If not, why not?

....

....

20 Suggest ways in which you believe the clearing procedures and practices could be improved.

....

....

Record of Achievement – Completion of Unit INC3	
Candidate's signature:	....
Assessor's signature:	....
Date:	....

Provide a counter or take-away service

Serve customers at the counter

Counter Service may be
- **Unassisted** – Customers help themselves to everything.
- **Partly Assisted** – Customers are served some items.

1 How should you greet customers at the counter?

....

....

2 When taking the order at the counter, look at the person and their facial expression. This will help you understand what the person is saying.

If the person has problems communicating what should you do?

....

....

3 When serving at the counter you must know the menu and the composition of the various items on the menu. The counter display must look attractive, for presentation is very important. What else should you check before service?

....

....

4 You must get to know different customers and how to cater for them. For example, those on special diets. Give two other examples.

....

....

5 If a portion of food is of a poor standard or looks cold, what should you do?

....

....

6 Always keep food cabinets topped up. Why?

....

....

....

7 Why must you not guess what is in a dish? For example, why would it be wrong to say to a customer 'the fruit pie doesn't usually have nuts in'.

....

....

8 Why is it important for service staff at the counter to offer accompaniments to suit the dish?

....

....

9 Repeating the order gives the customer a chance to confirm what they want. While doing so, what else could you ask them?

....

....

10 How can a service counter assistant help to promote sales?

....

....

11 Many customers do not like waiting at the counter. It is important to tell them about the waiting time. For example, the dish may be cooked to order, or more of the item is being sent from the kitchen. Give the customer the correct waiting time. Why?

....

....

12 When taking orders by phone, customers want their orders when they call or have them delivered. How should the telephone be answered?

13 If the customer on the telephone doesn't have a menu or know what the restaurant has to offer, what should you do?

Drive-thru take away

14 The person at the counter must have the order ready for the customer or make sure it is delivered on time. The customer's telephone number is important. Why?

15 If you do not recognise the address for delivery, what should you do?

....

....

16 How can the telephone number 1471 help the person at the counter?

....

....

17 For take-away, the service counter assistant is required to:

a obtain name and

....

b Suggest appropriate drinks and pro............... items

....

c repeat the or...............

d indicate where the customer may wait

....

On the telephone

a answer within the first 3 ....

introduce yourself and ....

b ask the customer what they would like to order, suggest value and any pro............... items

c repeat ....

d thank the customer for..

18 Some customers come into the restaurant and are not sure what they want to eat. Therefore the counter assistant should assist them in their choice.

This is an opportunity to s............... the products.

19 Some customers can get offended by over-sell. Why?

....

....

....

20 You must make the food you are describing interesting and irresistible.

Make the following sound more irresistible.

a 'would you like a drink?'

....

....

....

b 'would you like some apple pie?'

....

....

c 'would you like a large portion of soup?'

....

....

21 Persuasion is a gentle technique, so try not to be too pushy. Be natural and make the customer feel com................ .

22 Treat every customer as an individual and make them feel ....

Maintain counter and service areas

1 Portion control is important. Name 3 items of portion control equipment used on the counter.

a ....

b ....

c ....

2 How should a curry and rice dish be placed on the plate? Draw this in the circle on page 98.

3 Personal hygiene is important when serving on the counter. Using the correct equipment rather than using your hands is very important. List 4 other rules of personal hygiene.

....

....

....

....

4 Keep all hot food in containers covered during quiet periods. Why?

....

....

5 Always have a sample of the hot food on display. Why?

....

....

6 If a customer changes their mind after the food has been plated, always give them a clean plate. Why?

....

....

7 Hot and cold food must be at the correct temperature. What temperature should

a hot food be served at?

....

b cold food be served at?

....

8 Portion control is important, so that everyone knows where they stand.

- Customers get upset when their friends have got more or less than them.
- Chef's order to produce the exact number of p................
- Portion control is planned to budget costs.

9 Counter assistants must be aware of Health and Safety. Why?

....

....

10 It all comes down to you at the counter. If the product is not right then don't serve it!

Attractive counter displays are important to create the right impression. It is more difficult to maintain the presentation throughout the service period, so that the first and last customer both get a good impression.

Preparation and cleaning procedures are also a priority for maintaining service.

Essential points during service are:

a tables cleared regularly after customers have left

b chairs returned to ....

c trolleys clean and placed in the correct ....

d trolleys must be moved slowly and q................

e plates cleared of food and stacked ....

f cups emptied and stacked ....

g trolley never left unattended in the r................

h empty trays replaced with full – never fill up empty containers in front of c................

i correct utensils used when re................ food.

11 Always inform the kitchen staff when dishes are running out. Why?

....

....

12 Suggest ways to maintain the counter display during service.

....

....

....

13 How should you deal with rubbish and food waste on the counter?

....

....

....

....

14 After the restaurant has closed how should the counter be left?

....

....

....

15 How should the following be left after service?

a refrigerated counters

....

b stainless steel counters

....

c hot counters

....

d drinks machines

....

....

e sinks and floors

....

....

f tables in the restaurant

....

....

g cutlery, cleaning cloths and bins

....

....

....

Record of Achievement – Completion of Unit INC4	
Candidate's signature:	....
Assessor's signature:	....
Date:	....

UNIT 1ND1

Clean food production areas, equipment and utensils

Clean food production areas

Read: *Practical Cookery* pages 37–39

1 Why is it important that work is planned and time appropriately allocated to meet daily schedules?

....

....

....

2 Sinks and hand-basins must be clean and free-flowing to satisfy food hygiene regulations.

What hand washing facilities must also be available in the kitchen?

....

....

3 Work surfaces, tables and cutting boards must be kept clean at all times.

a How should they be cleaned?

....

b What are the dangers if they are not kept clean?

....

4 What protective clothing should be worn for cleaning tasks, and why?

....

5 Floors and walls must be clean and the floors kept dry.

What is the danger of a wet floor, or if fat has been spilled?

....

6 Why should

sink waste gullies be checked regularly and cleaned of any blockages?

....

traps be used to collect tea leaves, grease and other debris, and be emptied and cleaned regularly?

....

shelves, cupboards and drawers be emptied and cleaned weekly?

....

7 Correct cleaning equipment and materials must be used. The cleaning specification should be supplied by your employer, but if you are ever in doubt about which, or how much, cleaning agent to use, what should you do?

....

8 Write out the correct procedure for the disposal of rubbish and waste food.

....

....

9 Why should rubbish not be allowed to accumulate outside a building?

....

....

10 Which is preferable: paper or plastic-lined bins which are destroyed with the rubbish, or unlined bins? Why?

....

....

11 What is a waste-master?

....

12 There are 6 good reasons why waste must be handled and disposed of correctly. Complete the list below:

- to comply with the law
- to avoid creating a fire hazard
- to prevent accidents
- to avoid pollution of the environment
- ....
- ....

13 Metal, painted and glass surfaces, floor and wall tiles, and vinyl or linoleum floor coverings must be cleaned to comply with Health and Safety legislation, food hygiene legislation and procedures laid down by your establishment.

Give 3 main reasons for cleaning:

- safeguard the quality of the finished product
- ....
- ....

In catering, there are 2 levels of cleanliness. One is physical cleanliness, the other is:

....

Name 4 factors which affect the quality of cleaning:

- temperature
- ....
- ....
- ....

State how you clean your food production areas after a training session or service.

....

....

....

14 Why should areas which are being cleaned be carefully marked?

....

15 Why should the cleaning of food production areas be carried out as soon as possible after use?

....

16 Why should cleaning equipment be stored separately from food items?

....

17 Why should detergents never be used in food areas?

....

18 Why should separate cleaning equipment be used for floors and work surfaces?

....

....

Clean food production equipment

Read: *Practical Cookery* pages 39–43

1 Food production equipment must be correctly turned off and dismantled before and during cleaning.
Why is this essential?

....

2 In order to satisfy Health, Safety and food regulations, equipment must be clean, dry and correctly re-assembled.

Why is this essential, in particular with gas stoves?

....

3 Always use the correct cleaning equipment and materials as specified by your employer. Equipment must be correctly stored after cleaning.

How should saucepans be stored, and why?

....

....

4 Ovens, hobs, ranges, griddles, grids, salamanders, fryers, bainsmarie and hotplates must all be cleaned after each service in order to comply with Health and Safety legislation, food hygiene legislation and all relevant procedures laid down by your employer.

Why are people reluctant to clean equipment if it is difficult to re-assemble?

....

....

Equipment should be so designed to protect the contents from external contamination. What does this mean?

....

....

Equipment must be designed, constructed and finished to enable it to be

....

....

5 Why should faults and maintenance requirements be reported to the supervisor?

....

6 Why is it important to follow manufacturers' instructions when using cleaning materials and equipment?

....

7 What are the dangers of storing cleaning materials in incorrectly labelled containers?

....

8 Why should disinfectants never be used in food areas?

....

Clean food production utensils

Read: *Practical Cookery* pages 41–43

1 What are the different procedures for cleaning, drying and storing of utensils?

....

....

2 Why should strainers and sieves be washed immediately after each use?

....

If saucepans are difficult to clean, what is the best procedure to use before washing them?

....

Why should scouring pads never be used on stainless steel?

....

Why should wooden items never be allowed to soak in water?

....

3 Why is it important to follow manufacturers' instructions when using cleaning materials and equipment?

....

4 Why should cleaning materials always be stored in correctly labelled containers?

....

5 Why should mechanical equipment be turned off before cleaning?

....

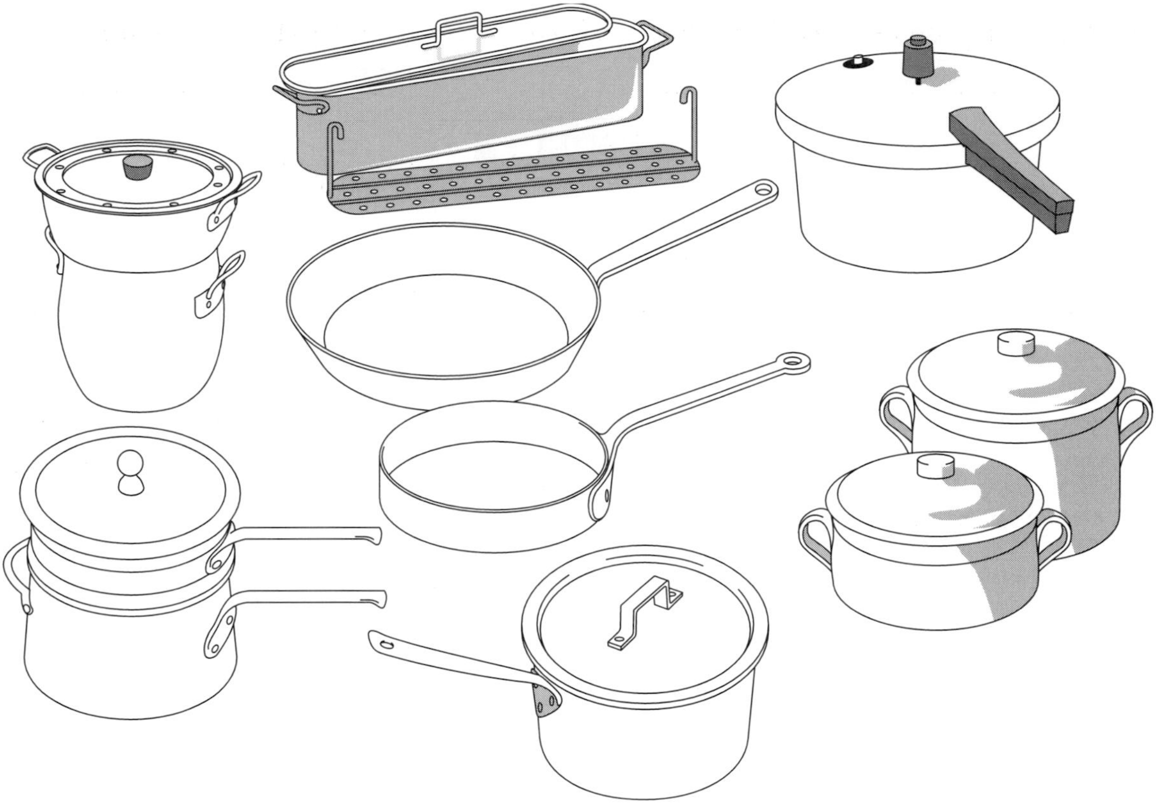

6 Why should equipment be dismantled before cleaning and correctly re-assembled after cleaning?

....

7 What extra care is required when cleaning Teflon-coated items?

....

8 How is small equipment washed and treated in your establishment or training centre?

....

....

....

....

Does the kitchen where you are training have a sterilisation sink for food utensils?

If the answer is yes, at what temperature does it operate?

....

9 What purpose does washing-up liquid play in cleaning small kitchen utensils?

....

Small utensils may cross-contaminate. What does this mean, and how can it be avoided?

....

....

....

....

10 Arc you able to suggest ways in which small equipment could be better handled and treated in your establishment?

....

....

11 Why does the following equipment cause specific cleaning problems?

Conical strainer ....

Fine wooden sieve ....

Manual can opener ....

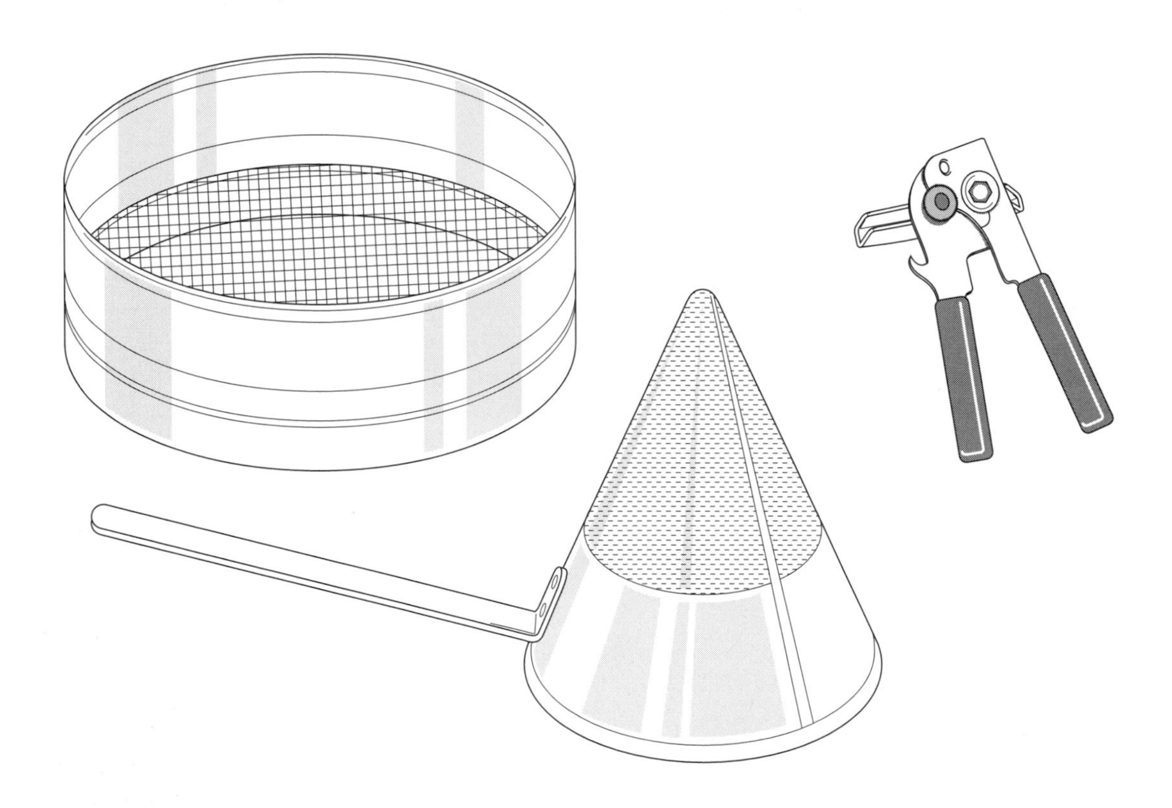

Record of Achievement – Completion of Unit IND1	
Candidate's signature:	....
Assessor's signature:	....
Date:	....

UNIT
IND3

Prepare and microwave food

Prepare food for microwave cooking

Read: *Practical Cookery* pages 106–108

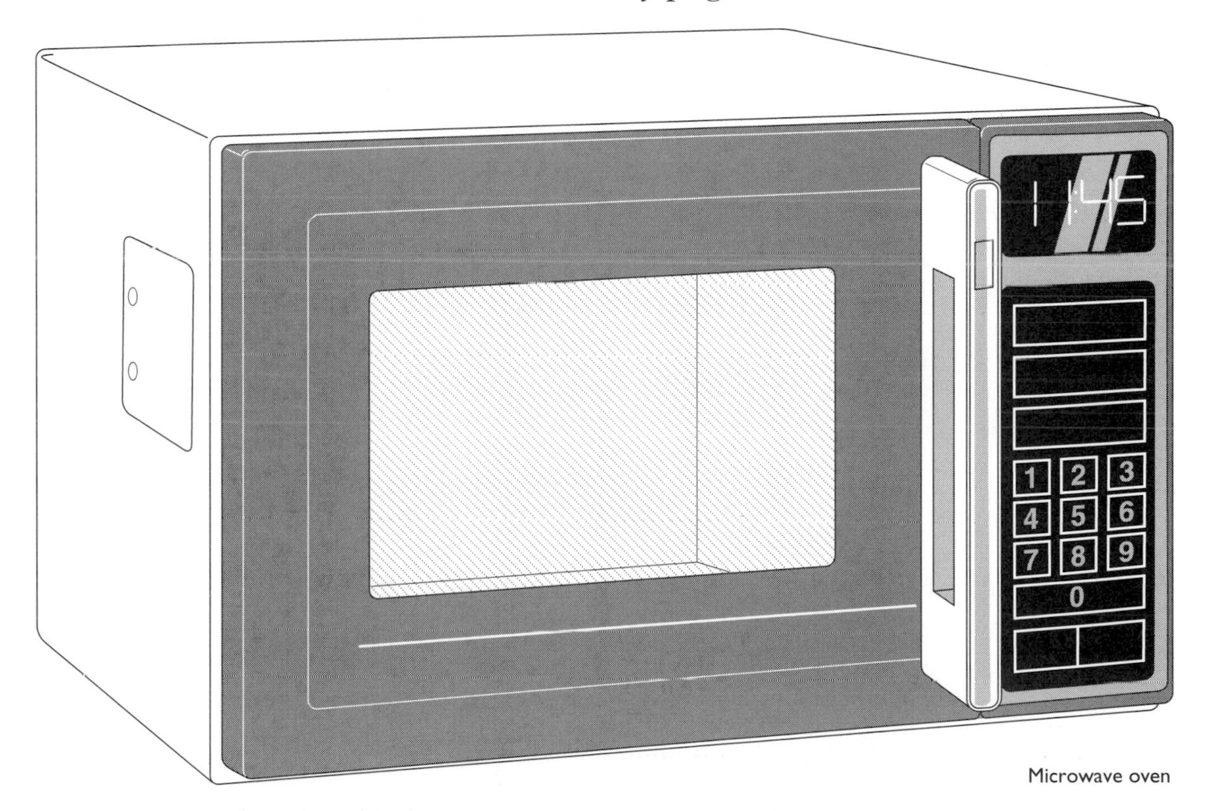

Microwave oven

1 Cooking time is much less when using a microwave oven.

True ☐ **False** ☐

2 A microwave oven can be used for defrosting food.

True ☐ **False** ☐

3 Microwave cookery can be economical on electricity.

True ☐ **False** ☐

4 Hot meals can be made available 24 hours a day and completely operated on a self-service basis, thereby reducing costs and increasing customer satisfaction.

Give an example of an establishment which could use a microwave oven to serve hot meals all day and all night.

....

....

5 Food hygiene is very important when preparing foods for microwave cookery.

True ☐ **False** ☐

6 How should foods which are not going to be microwaved immediately be stored. Tick [✓] the right answer.

a in a cupboard ☐

b in a food store ☐

c in a deep freeze ☐

d in a refrigerator ☐

7 Preparation areas and equipment must be cleaned after use. Why?

....

....

....

8 If you find that the microwave oven is not working, who should you report it to?

....

9 Name 3 types of convenience foods which you could microwave.

....

....

....

10 Only small amounts of food can be cooked, defrosted or reheated at a time.

True ☐ **False** ☐

11 Most microwave ovens do not colour foods, but there are some ovens that have a built-in colouring unit.

True ☐ **False** ☐

12 Microwaves can penetrate food only to a depth of 4 cm ($1\frac{1}{2}$ in).

True ☐ **False** ☐

Microwave energy is a high-frequency power similar to energy which carries television signals from the broadcasting transmitter to the receiver, but operating at much higher frequencies.

13 In a television set

Television

The Cathode ray tube is used in a microwave oven

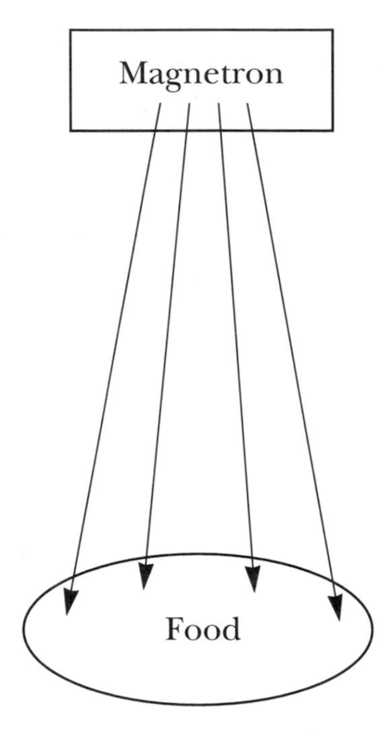

The tube is called a Magn............... which generates the microwaves.

When the microwave oven is switched on the invisible microwaves enter the oven and pass through the food.

The oven is lined with metal because microwaves are reflected back into the food.

14 Microwaves are reflected by metal.

True ☐ **False** ☐

15 Microwaves are transmitted through glass and ceramics. Name 1 other material that microwaves pass through.

....

16 Microwaves are not absorbed by food.

True ☐ **False** ☐

17 When your hands are cold, if you rub them together quickly heat is generated by friction.

Food is comprised of small particles known as **molecules** and when microwaves pass through the food they rub together quickly, or agitate the molecules, causing friction and heat which .... the food.

18 For safety reasons the seal round the microwave oven door must always be intact. On no account should a microwave oven be used if the seal is not perfect. Why?

....

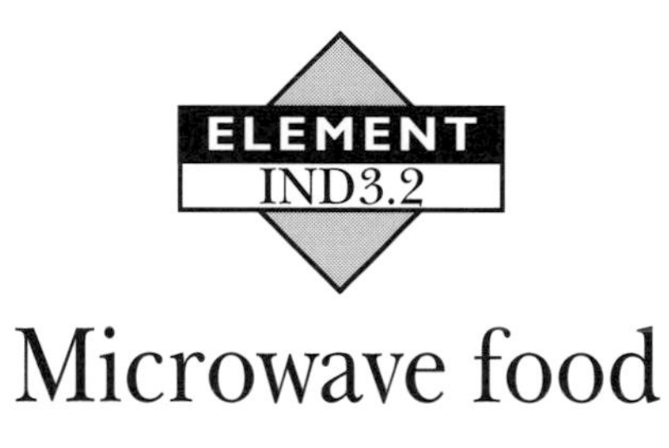

Microwave food

1 Is it possible to cook a large thick item of food by microwaving?

Yes ☐ **No** ☐

2 Does the air in the microwave oven get hot?

Yes ☐ **No** ☐

3 Placing metal in some types of microwave oven will damage them.

True ☐ **False** ☐

4 The manufacturer's instructions must always be followed.

True ☐ **False** ☐

5 How should a microwave oven be cleaned?

....

....

....

....

6 Scouring pads and abrasives should not be used in microwave ovens. Why?

....

....

7 If the microwave oven has a separate air filter should this be washed separately?

Yes ☐ **No** ☐

8 Why is the use of a microwave oven economical?

....

....

9 Name 3 kinds of material from which containers can be made for use in a microwave oven.

....

....

....

10 Suggest 2 uses of a microwave oven.

....

....

11 Give 2 examples of cookery when a microwave oven is not suitable.

....

....

12 Eggs must not be cooked in their shells or they will b...............

13 Foods, when cooking in a microwave oven, when possible should be covered to reduce condensation and splu...............ing.

14 Baked potatoes and whole unpeeled apples must have the skin pie............... in order to release pr............... and prevent them bur................

15 Certain foods must be removed when underdone to finish cooking, so standing time is important. Name 1 food which needs to stand.

....

Name 1 food which does not need to stand.

....

16 Foods with a high water content cook faster than those which contain less water.

True ☐ **False** ☐

17 Why should microwave ovens be regularly inspected by a trained engineer?

....

....

18 Time and temperature are important when preparing pre-prepared convenience food for microwave cooking. Why?

a to make sure the food reaches a safe temperature to ensure all bacteria are destroyed.

b too long a cooking will affect the qu............... of the finished dish.

19 Working, preparing and cooking microwave food in dirty areas will cause contamination. Contamination could be caused by:

a dirty surfaces

b using the same chopping board for raw and cooked food

c ....

d ....

20 To produce the dish properly and to present it correctly, the chef or cook must:

a follow the recipe and method

b refer to a standard photo................

This is to ensure that all microwave dishes are prepared to the correct standard every .... an order is received.

Record of Achievement – Completion of Unit IND3	
Candidate's signature:	....
Assessor's signature:	....
Date:	....

UNIT
IND4
Prepare and fry food

Prepare food for frying

Read: *Practical Cookery* pages 99–105: 261–264

1 Before frying foods, why is it essential to ensure that preparation areas and suitable equipment are hygienic and ready for use? How would you do this?

....

....

2 List the items of equipment required for deep frying.

....

....

....

....

3 Name the food items suitable for deep, shallow and stir frying.

....

....

....

....

....

....

4 Why is it important that food items to be fried are of the correct type, quality and quantity?

....

....

....

....

5 Give examples to illustrate the answer to Question 4.

For example, fried fillets of plaice – should be of equal size to ensure uniformity of cooking, should be fresh (or freshly frozen) without any stale smell, taint or slime and should be of sufficient quantity to fulfil requirements.

....

....

....

....

6 Describe how the following items are suitably prepared for frying.

a battered fish fillets

....

b flour, egg and crumbed chicken pieces

....

c apple fritters

....

d chipped potatoes

....

7 Name 6 items of food prepared for frying and state in each case where they should be stored if they are not to be cooked until several hours later.

....

....

....

....

....

....

8 Why is it essential that preparation areas and equipment are cleaned after each use?

....

....

9 Read *The Theory of Catering* page 398.

What is the correct procedure for cleaning a

a deep fat fryer?

....

....

b frying pan

....

....

c wok

....

....

Stir fry

10 Why is it important that unexpected situations are dealt with effectively and appropriate people informed where necessary?

....

....

....

11 How would you deal with the following and who would you inform in each case?

a After frying a batch of croquette potatoes you found they were covered in burnt particles.

....

....

b You found the friture was overheating.

....

....

c The friture spilled over while chips were being fried.

....

....

d Give suggested reasons for **a**, **b** and **c**.

....

....

12 Why is it essential that all work is carried out in an organised and efficient manner in line with appropriate organisational procedures and legal requirements?

....

....

13 What safe working practices should be followed when preparing pre-prepared and convenience food for frying?

....

....

....

14 What are the main contamination threats when preparing and storing food for frying? Give 3 examples of bad practice that you have observed.

....

....

....

15 State good reasons why time and temperature control is important when preparing food for frying.

....

....

....

16 If prepared food is not stored at the required safe temperature but is left on a shelf or table in a warm kitchen, what is likely to happen?

....

....

....

17 Write out the methods of preparation for:

a fillets of plaice meunière

....

....

b sauté potatoes

....

....

c whitebait

....

....

d chipped potatoes

....

....

e stir fry of mixed vegetables

....

....

f a stir fry dish of your choice

....

....

18 What is the essential part of the preparation for food to be stir fried?

....

....

....

....

....

....

ELEMENT
IND4.2

Fry food

Read: *Practical Cookery* pages 99–105

1 Describe the 10 Safety Rules for deep frying.

....

....

....

....

....

....

....

....

....

....

2 What is meant by the 'flash point' of a frying pan of deep fat or oil?

....

....

3 What are the signs to look for when deep fat or oil is approaching 'flash point'?

....

....

4 If the fat or oil reaches 'flash point' what should you immediately do?

....

....

5 Why is it important to keep cooking areas and equipment hygienic when frying food? Give a detailed answer with examples of bad practice you have observed.

....

....

....

....

6 What are the main contamination threats when frying and storing pre prepared and convenience food?

....

....

7 Write about the importance of time and temperature control in deep frying.

....

....

....

....

8 What is meant by 'recovery time' when deep frying?

....

....

9 How can you tell when the following items are cooked to dish requirements?

a Sauté potatoes

....

....

b Croquette potatoes

....

....

c Cod fillet in batter

....

....

d Flour, egg and crumbed chicken breasts (shallow fried)

....

....

e Banana fritters

....

....

f Vegetable stir fry

....

....

10 Which fats or oils can contribute to Healthy Eating Practice?

....

....

....

....

11 Describe 4 ways of shallow frying.

....

....

....

....

12 What is the difference between:

a chicken sauté

....

....

b fried chicken breast

....

....

13 What additions are made to a dish of fried fish when it is termed 'meunière'?

....

....

14 What is the purpose of using a batter when deep frying fish?

....

....

15 What other forms of coating may be used for deep frying fish?

....

....

Record of Achievement – Completion of Unit IND4	
Candidate's signature:	....
Assessor's signature:	....
Date:	....

UNIT
IND9

Prepare vegetables and fruit

Prepare vegetables

Read: *Practical Cookery* pages 517–580

1 Why must preparation areas and equipment be hygienic and ready for use? Explain how you would do this.

....

....

....

2 If the vegetables to be prepared are not of the correct

a type

b quality

c quantity

what is *likely to happen*?

....

....

....

....

....

....

3 Vegetables must always be prepared using appropriate methods to meet dish requirements.

For example, potatoes for mash should not be cut too small otherwise they may absorb too much water and result in a soggy mash.

Give 3 other examples of incorrect preparation methods, each for a different vegetable and state in each case the likely result.

a ....

b ....

c ....

4 When the following vegetables are prepared for use later in the day, how should they be stored?

a Brussel sprouts ....

b Tomatoes ready for grilling...

c Peeled potatoes for Duchess potatoes ....

d Diced carrots ....

5 Unexpected situations must always be dealt with effectively and the appropriate people informed where necessary. What would you do regarding the following:

a out of 60 lbs potatoes, a third are in a mushy condition.

....

....

b cabbage is full of a green fly type of pest and smells strong

....

....

c when cutting carrots some are hard and woody

....

....

d Give 3 other examples from your experience

....

....

....

6 a Why is it important that all work is carried out in an organised and efficient manner in line with appropriate organisational procedures and legal requirements?

....

....

b Give 3 examples of poor organisation that you have observed.

....

....

....

7 List the quality points for

a root vegetables ....

b tubers ....

c bulbs ....

d leaves ....

e stems ....

f vegetable fruits ....

8 All vegetables should be thoroughly washed before being cooked. What are the exceptions to this rule?

....

9 Why does spinach sometimes need washing 3 to 4 times, changing the water each time?

....

10 Why should potatoes be peeled as thinly as possible?

....

11 Which of the root vegetables are best peeled with a knife?

....

12 Name 3 different pieces of equipment for slicing vegetables.

....

13 Should vegetables requiring trimming be trimmed before being washed?

....

14 What is the best method for chopping onions?

....

15 What are the main contamination threats when preparing vegetables? Give examples to illustrate your answer.

....

....

16 What are the potential dangers of not thoroughly washing vegetables?

....

....

17 Why must washed vegetables be kept separate from unwashed vegetables?

....

18 List the quality points for

a root vegetables

....

....

b green vegetables

....

19 How should the different types of vegetables be stored to keep them in the best condition?

....

....

....

....

20 How frequently should vegetables in store be checked?

....

21 The fresher the vegetables the better the flavour, so that ideally they should not be stored at all.

True ☐ **False** ☐

22 What is likely to happen if blemished vegetables are not removed from perfect produce?

....

....

23 Why should vegetables be removed or loosened from any plastic wrapping?

24 Why is it essential to follow suppliers' instructions when storing frozen vegetables?

....

....

Prepare fruit

Read: *Practical Cookery* pages 589–593

1 What can be the result if preparation and storage areas and equipment are not kept clean and in a hygienic condition?

....

....

2 What are the main contamination threats when preparing fruits? Give specific examples to illustrate your answer.

....

....

....

3 Why is it essential to thoroughly wash and keep washed items separate from unwashed items?

....

....

4 List 10 quality points to look for in fruit.

....

....

....

....

....

....

....

....

....

....

5 How should the following fruits be stored?

a Hard fruits (for example, apples) ....

b Soft fruits (for example, raspberries) ....

c Stone fruits (for example, peaches) ....

d Citrus fruits (for example, oranges, lemons) ....

e Bananas ....

6 Why is it essential that blemished fruit should be immediately separated from perfect produce?

....

....

7 Why should fruit be removed or loosened from plastic wrapping?

8 Why is it important to follow suppliers' instructions on storing frozen fruit?

....

9 What type of apples are used for apple fritters and how are the apples prepared?

....

....

10 a List 8 fruits suitable for a fresh fruit salad and state how each are prepared.

....

....

....

....

....

....

....

....

b Why is it essential that fruit for fruit salad be at peak ripeness?

....

11 How should gooseberries be prepared before cooking?

....

12 How should rhubarb be prepared for cooking?

....

13 What is the preparation for black and red currants?

....

14 Are apples and pears best peeled using a sharp small knife or a fine peeler? Why?

....

Record of Achievement – Completion of Unit IND9	
Candidate's signature:	....
Assessor's signature:	....
Date:	....

Prepare, cook and assemble food for service

Prepare food and kitchen areas for service

In order that the service period runs smoothly, attention has to be paid to the preparation time. The better prepared the kitchen is the better and more smoothly the service will operate, thus avoiding excessive pressure on the staff.

1 Why is it important to clear down food preparation areas before service?

....

....

2 All items of small equipment must be in place before the service. Write down the list of equipment you are required to lay out before service. For example: ladles, serving spoons

....

....

....

....

3 It is important to check that the food for the service is of the correct type, quality and quantity required in the menu.

Write down a quality specification for a dish that features on a menu in your establishment.

For example: 30 portions of Brown Beef Stew with Noodles:

Brown beef stew prepared to standard recipe, sauce should be a rich brown colour, finished with chopped parsley served in a $\frac{1}{2}$ gastronome stainless steel container. Check temperature – must be over 75 °C. Freshly prepared noodles, seasoned, brushed with butter, placed in a $\frac{1}{4}$ gastronome tray.

....

....

....

....

....

4 If the food is not of the right type or quantity for service, who should you report this to?

....

5 Why is the temperature of the food for service of particular importance?

....

....

6 Food which is not at the correct temperature must be returned to the kitchen.

True ☐ **False** ☐

7 Give an example of any food items which only require defrosting prior to service.

....

....

8 How should food be defrosted prior to service?

....

9 The Food Safety (Temperature Control) Regulations 1995 state that foods which may be subject to microbiological multiplication must be held at no more than 8 °C or above ....

10 If waste is allowed to accumulate in food rooms there is a potential contamination threat from ....

11 What safety precautions have to be adhered to prior to the service starting?

....

....

....

12 List the convenience food items which have to be displayed on the food counter before service.

....

....

....

13 Name 4 items of service equipment

....

....

....

....

14 If you find that a piece of equipment is not working prior to the service, what should you do?

....

15 Why should cooked food which is not for immediate consumption be rapidly cooled and maintained at a safe temperature?

....

....

16 Which items of cooked food cause particular contamination threats prior and during service?

....

....

....

17 Hot cooked rice after service should be discarded. Why?

....

....

18 Which food poisoning bacteria is associated with the following foods?

Cooked rice ....

Cooked chicken ....

Egg based sauces ....

Cook and assemble food products for service

1 All food products must be assembled in a clean and hygienic environment. Why?

....

....

2 Portioning cooked food is very important for a number of reasons. Suggest 3 reasons.

a Food cost control

b ....

c ....

d ....

3 Name 4 food items which can be purchased portioned prior to cooking.

a Chicken Suprêmes

b ....

c ....

d ....

e ....

4 At which temperature should cooked food be reheated?

....

5 At which temperature should cooked food be held during service?

....

6 Name any foods which you are aware of which should be disposed of after service.

....

....

....

7 How should all ingredients for service be assembled and stored for service?

....

....

8 Give examples of 4 convenience foods which require assembly prior to service.

a Ice-cream desserts

b ....

c ....

d ....

9 If there is a problem with service ingredients, who should you inform?

....

10 If during the service period an item of food runs out, who should you inform? What other action should you take?

....

....

11 What Health and Safety precautions should you be aware of during service?

....

....

12 Being organised for service is extremely important to achieve an efficient operation. List the key factors which will lead to an organised service in your establishment.

All items ready and in place on time
....

All waste removed, all areas cleared down before service
....

....

....

....

....

13 Work planning and scheduling is also important to achieve an efficient organised operation. What is a work plan?

....

....

14 Write down an example of a simple work plan for a dish requiring cooking and assembly before service.

Name of dish: ....

Use the space on page 142 for your plan.

WORK PLAN:

15 Temperature of cooked and chilled food must be continually checked during service. Why?

....

....

16 All service areas should have wash-hand basins fitted. Why?

....

17 How can you encourage frequent hand washing?

....

....

18 Before or after the service food samples should be taken of all the cooked food. For what purpose?

....

....

19 If a hot cabinet breaks down during service, what should you do?

....

20 If a chiller or freezer cabinet breaks down during service, what should you do?

....

21 When there appears to be a problem with the chiller, it is important that you check the temperature of the food and the 'space temperature'. What is meant by the space temperature?

....

22 Why is the air temperature in the chiller of significant importance?

....

....

23 Why is it important to keep high standards of personal hygiene at all times but especially during the service period?

....

....

....

....

24 Cleaning equipment and maintaining a high standard of equipment cleanliness during service is also important. How should small items of equipment be kept during service?

....

....

25 To prevent the transfer of bacteria, certain precautions have to be taken during cooking and assembly, especially in relation to chef's knives and cutting boards. Name these precautions.

....

....

....

26 Food waste and packaging can accumulate during service. How should the disposal of both be organised?

....

....

....

....

Record of Achievement – Completion of Unit IND11	
Candidate's signature:	....
Assessor's signature:	....
Date:	....

UNIT

IND14

Prepare and griddle food

Prepare food for griddling

Read: *Practical Cookery* pages 96–99

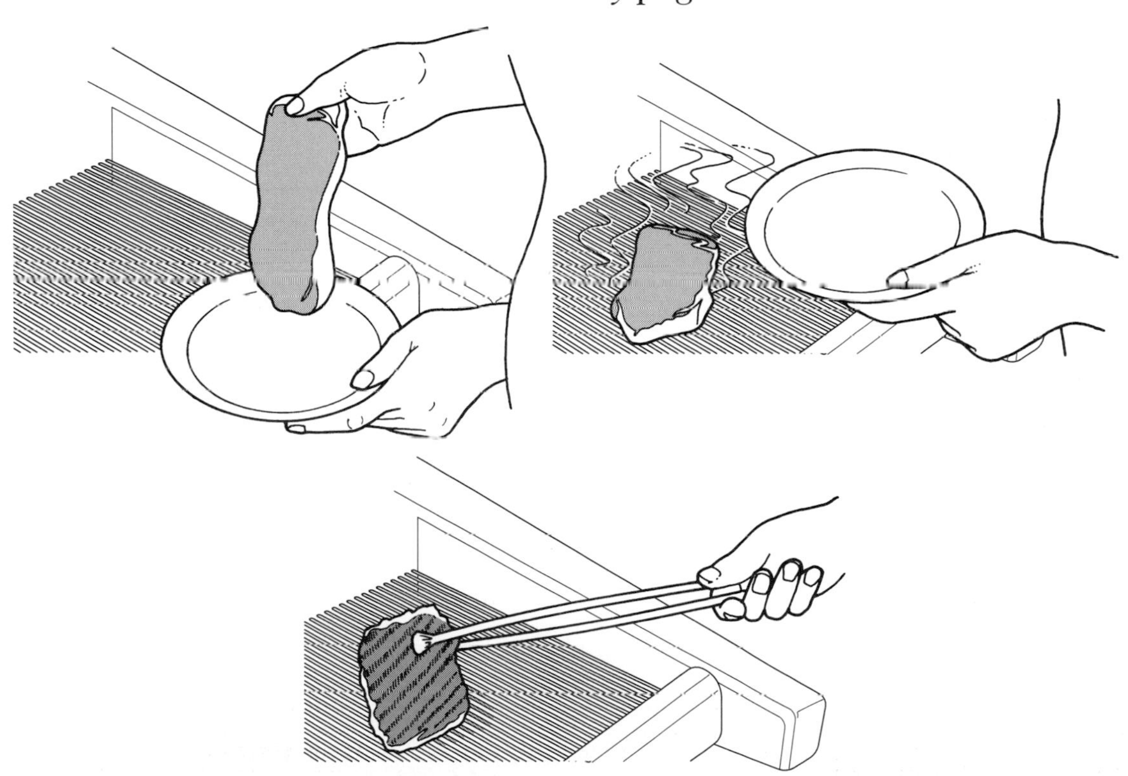

1 Before preparing food for cooking on the griddle, all food preparation areas must be clean and hygienic to prevent the food becoming contaminated. Which type of bacteria are harmful?

Food p..

2 All preparation and cooking areas must be cleaned after use. Why?

....

3 If food has been prepared and is not required to be cooked on the griddle immediately, where should it be stored?

....

4 The law requires a chef or cook to prepare all food in a hygienic manner.

True ☐ **False** ☐

5 To prepare food properly and according to the law, contamination can be prevented by colour coding items of equipment. What item of equipment should you colour code?

....

....

6 Complete the following table:

Colour	Denotes the following food
Red	Raw meat
Blue	
Green	
Brown	

7 Suggest 4 items of fresh food which may be cooked on a griddle.

....

....

....

....

8 Suggest 2 items of convenience or prepared food that may be cooked on a griddle.

....

....

9 How should the following be prepared before being cooked on a griddle.

Courgettes ....

....

Aubergine ....

....

Onions ....

....

Sirloin steak ....

....

Rainbow trout ....

....

10 If the food for griddling is not of the right quality, what should you do?

....

11 If the griddling equipment is not working efficiently, what should you do?

....

12 All food for griddling should be placed on clean trays in order, after being prepared. If not for immediate use the trays should be stored in the refrigerator. Items for griddling are taken out when needed.

Preparing and storing food in this way before cooking and service is known as

....

13 Draw a tray of prepared food items for griddling. Name each item of food. Concentrate on an organised layout.

14 How should a small whole trout be prepared for griddling?

....

....

Griddle food

Read: *Practical Cookery* pages 99–102

1 Traditional griddle plates are black iron plates which are used for frying. Modern griddle plates are grooved. This allows the food to be turned around to give it a criss-cross pattern. This is known as Quadrillage. This method also appears on menus and in recipes as a form of grilling.

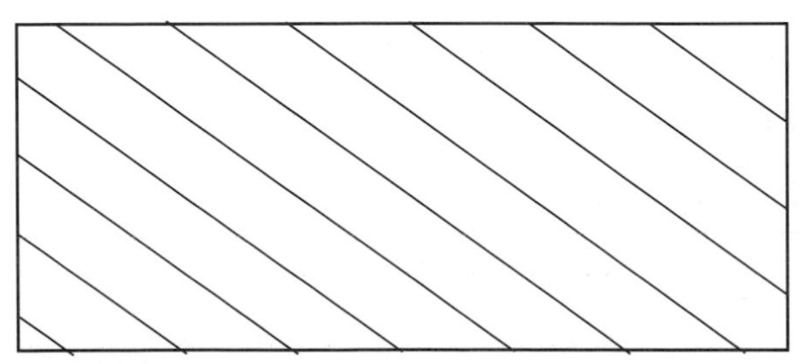

These plates are placed directly on the heat.
Name a dish using this method of cooking.

....

2 When working with the griddle plate, we must be aware of Health and Safety. The following precautions must be adhered to:

- Never use too much oil.
- Take special care to control the heat.
- Make sure the food for griddling is dry.
- Know where the fire blanket or fire extinguisher is located.

Name 2 other safety precautions.

....

....

3 Hygiene is also important when griddling food. The following hygiene procedure must be followed:

- Wash hands regularly.
- Make sure all protective clothing is worn correctly and is clean.
- Handle food as little as possible.

Name 2 other hygiene procedures.

....

....

4 How should the griddle be cleaned after use?

....

....

5 Time and temperature is important when griddling food.

a To ensure food is cooked properly and achieve the correct texture.

b To kill harmful ....

c ....

d ....

6 How can you tell the following is cooked properly on the griddle:

Sliced bacon ....

....

Hamburgers..

....

Sausages..

....

Small veal escalopes ....

....

7 Non-stick griddle pans may be used to reduce the amount of fat or oil in cooking.

a Why should we want to do this?

....

b Teflon coated griddle plates are non-stick.

True ☐ **False** ☐

c What other ways are we able to reduce the fat content?

....

....

8 Name the types of operation which may use griddle plates.

....

....

9 Griddle cooking can be classed as a fast method of cooking.

True ☐ **False** ☐

10 Pancakes may also be cooked on a griddle.

True ☐ **False** ☐

11 Name another pastry item that may be cooked on a griddle.

....

12 Write down any items you have recently cooked on a griddle.

....

....

....

....

....

Record of Achievement – Completion of Unit IND14	
Candidate's signature:	....
Assessor's signature:	....
Date:	....